CONTENTS

FOLK AND ART SONGS

THE DITTY BAG

by

JANET E. TOBITT

Included in this volume of 172 songs are 54 songs of
a new compilation plus contents of "Yours for a Song,"
"Sing Me Your Song, O " and "Notes for Song Leaders."

Price $1.⁰⁰

FOREWORD

This book contains songs of some thirty countries, including a dozen or so of Latin-American origin, selected for their inherent beauty or ready appeal. Music speaks in a universal language of human needs and aspirations; it is a unifying force in a chaotic world. When mothers sing "Go to Sleepy," "Willie, Willie, Will," "Lustukru," or "Tutú Marambá" in widely separated parts of the globe they are merely saying the same thing in slightly different ways. The Swedish "Farmer and the Crow" and the English "Red Herring" tell equally tall stories of carcasses put to fabulous use; invitations to dance, walk or flirt only vary according to native use and custom.

It is hoped that in this compilation leaders of informal singing will be able to find material for the planned program and the unexpected demand. Notes and words are not enough; real understanding of a song, however simple, comes from a study of all its implications. Imaginative interpretation on the part of a leader inspires lively group response and intelligent singing generally means good tone quality.

Thanks are due to the many publishers and individuals whose helpful co-operation has made this collection possible. Great care has been taken to trace copyrights to their correct sources. If, despite this, any copyright has been unwittingly infringed, we beg that we may be pardoned and informed in order that in future editions the mistake may be rectified.

For guide to the pronunciation of Spanish words see page 20

ROUNDS AND CANONS

HYMNS AND CAROLS

THE DITTY BAG

BLOW ON THE SEA SHELL

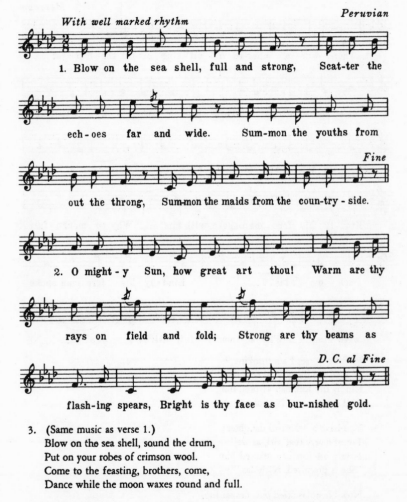

With well marked rhythm   *Peruvian*

1. Blow on the sea shell, full and strong, Scat-ter the
ech-oes far and wide. Sum-mon the youths from
out the throng, Sum-mon the maids from the coun-try-side.

2. O might-y Sun, how great art thou! Warm are thy
rays on field and fold; Strong are thy beams as
flash-ing spears, Bright is thy face as bur-nished gold.

3. (Same music as verse 1.)
   Blow on the sea shell, sound the drum,
   Put on your robes of crimson wool.
   Come to the feasting, brothers, come,
   Dance while the moon waxes round and full.

The above song was part of the mid-summer festivities held in the great square in Cuzco. It was customary to summon the people by blowing on sea shells.

THE BUMPKIN
(El Charro)

Mexican

1. There was a char-ro a-sit-ting___ On the fence of a
wide cor-ral.___ There was a char-ro a-sit-ting___
On the fence of a wide cor-ral.___
Kind-ly his fore-man spoke with him,___ "Why so mourn-ful,
Nich-o-las?"___ Kind-ly his fore-man spoke
with him,___ "Why so mourn-ful, Nich-o-las?"___

2. I need a horse, I am thinking,
   A good saddle, a good coat too.
   Kindly the foreman assured him,
   "All is yours, my Nicholas."

3. You have a beautiful daughter;
   I must marry that girl, as well.
   Firmly his foreman assured him,
   "She is promised, Nicholas."

4. Now Nicholas cried out, despairing,
   Down the canyon himself would throw.
   Kindly the foreman suggested,
   "Make it head first, Nicholas!"

From "The Latin-American Song Book," copyright 1942. Used by permission of Ginn and Company, owners of the copyright.

TUTÚ MARAMBÁ
Lullaby

English version by A. D. Z.   *Brazilian*

Expressively, in swaying rhythm

Tu - tú Ma-ram-bá,   if   you come this way,   The

ba - by's_ fa - ther will   chase you a - way;   'Tu-

tú   Ma - ram - bá,   if   you_ come this way,   The

Fine

ba - by's_ fa - ther will   chase you a - way.

Expressively

Go to sleep, my ba - by, love-ly   lit-tle pet of mine,

mf

Beau-ti - ful and hap-py be, O   lit-tle child of mine._ A-

A little faster

ra - nha Ta - ta - nha, A - ra - nha Ta - ti - nha, Ta-

p

tú your house is scratch-ing to   see if you are sleep-ing, A-

ra - nha Ta - ta - nha, A - ra - nha Ta - ti - nha, Ta-

poco rit.

tu   will   be glad when he   finds you are sleep - ing.

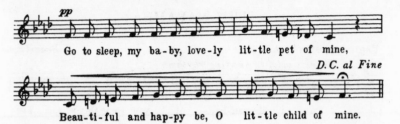

Go to sleep, my ba-by, love-ly lit-tle pet of mine,

D. C. al Fine

Beau-ti-ful and hap-py be, O lit-tle child of mine.

Tutú Marambá is an imaginary frightening character like our "bogeyman." Aranha Tatanha and Tatinha is a spider in Brazilian fairy tales. Tatú is an armadillo of like significance.

From "Singing America." Used by permission of the National Recreation Association, owners of the copyright, and C. C. Birchard and Co., publishers.

SAN SERENI

Puerto Rico
Singing Game

San Se-re-ní de la bue-na, bue-na vi-da,

ha-cen a-sí, a-sí los za-pa-te-ros, a-

sí, a-sí, a-sí, a-sí me gus-ta a mí.

San Serení is the children's saint. The words mean literally "San Serení of the good life, the shoemakers go thus and so it pleases me."

ACTION. The players hold hands and skip to the left around one chosen to be in the center who pantomimes the motions of a shoemaker. After the word "zapateros" (shoemakers) the others stand still and copy the actions of the center player on the words "así, así, así, así."

On the repetition of the song other players go to the center in turn and in any order perform the motions of different occupations e.g. los carpinteros (carpenters), las lavanderas (washerwomen), las planchadoras (ironers), los campaneros (bellringers), las costureras (dressmakers), los jardineros (gardeners), los barqueros (boatmen), etc.

RIQUI RAN

Translated by J. Olcutt Sanders   *Latin - American*

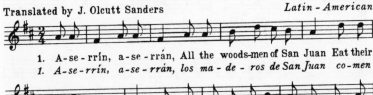

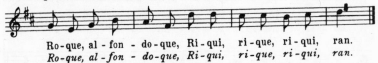

1. A-se-rrín, a-se-rrán, All the woods-men of San Juan Eat their
1. A-se-rrín, a-se-rrán, los ma-de-ros de San Juan co-men

cheese and eat their pan. Those from Ri-que al-fe-ñi-que; Those from
que-so, co-men pan. Los de Ri-que al-fe-ñi que; los de

Ro-que, al-fon-do-que, Ri-qui, ri-que, ri-qui, ran.
Ro-que, al-fon-do-que, Ri-qui, ri-que, ri-qui, ran.

2. Aserrín, asserán. All the bees fly hither, yon;
   Gather nectar for their pan,
   Sipping from the flowers of Rique
   Nectar sweet as alfeñique,
   Just as honey combs of Roque
   Look like loaves of alfondoque. Riqui, rique, riqui ran.

3. Aserrín, aserrán. Where have all the children gone?
   They have put their night-gowns on.
   They will dream of alfeñique
   As the children dream in Rique,
   And to-morrow alfondoque
   They will eat with those from Roque. Riqui, rique, riqui ran.

2. *Aserrín, aserrán. Las abejas vienen, van;*
   Miel laboran para el pan.
   Liban flores las de Rique
   Cual almíbar de alfeñique,
   Y el panal de los de Roque
   Se parece a un alfondoque. Riqui, rique, riqui ran.

3. *Aserrín, aserrán. Los chiquillos ¿dónde están?*
   Todos a dormir se van.
   Soñarán con alfeñique
   Como sueñan los de Rique
   Y mañana un alfondoque
   Comerán con los de Roque. Riqui, rique, riqui ran.

Alfeñique, (ahl-fay-nyee'-kay),—white sugar candy.
Alfondoque, (ahl-fohn-doh'-kay),—brown loaf sugar.
Pan, (pahn),—bread; also honey in the comb.

PERICA

Translated by J. Olcutt Sanders

Chilean

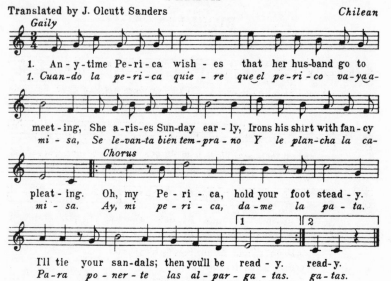

1. An-y-time Pe-ri-ca wish-es that her hus-band go to
1. *Cuan-do la pe-ri-ca quie-re que_el pe-ri-co va-ya a-*

meet-ing, She a-ris-es Sun-day ear-ly, Irons his shirt with fan-cy
mi-sa, Se le-van-ta bién tem-pra-no Y le plan-cha la ca-

Chorus

pleat-ing.   Oh, my   Pe-ri-ca,   hold your   foot stead-y.
mi-sa.   Ay, mi   pe-ri-ca,   da-me   la   pa-ta.

I'll tie   your san-dals; then you'll be   read-y.   read-y.
Pa-ra   po-ner-te   las al-par-ga-tas.   ga-tas.

2. Anytime Perica wishes
   That her husband eat his dinner,
   She knows how he likes it parboiled,
   Neither of the two grows thinner.

3. Anytime Perica wishes
   That her husband show attention,
   Then she doffs her dowdy housedress,
   Dons a blouse that merits mention.

2. *Cuando la perica quiere*
   Que el perico coma_arroz
   Le salcocha la comida
   Y se la comen los dos.

3. *Cuando la perica quiere*
   Que_el perico se_enamore,
   Se quita, la plumas viejas
   Y se vista de colores.
   Perica,—diminutive of Petra; also a small parrot.

By permission of the Cooperative Recreation Service, Delaware, Ohio.

FROM THE WHITE EARTH
(De blanca tierra)

English by A.D.Z.   *Bolivian*

All from the white earth we've come to-geth-er, All up from the
De blan-ca tier - ra   he - mos ve - ni - do, De nues-tra tier-

earth we've come to-geth-er,   From   la - bor   all
ra   he - mos ve - ni - do,   Can   sa - dos,   ren -

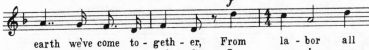

wea-ry, but for our   God   As four we have come, we've come to-
di - dos por el Se -   ñor   Y en-tre cua - tro   he - mos ve-

geth-er,   As four we have come, we've come to-geth-er, An-oth-er
ni - do,   Y en-tre cua - tro   he - mos ve - ni - do, O-tro se ha

stray-ing from   the road be - hind us,   Rov-ing a - far.
que-da - do   en el   ca - mi - no,   A ro - de - ar.

From "Singing America." Used by permission of the National Recreation Association,
owners of the copyright and C. C. Birchard and Co., publishers.

MI CHACRA
(My Farm)

Arranged by Sarabelle Hicks   *Argentinian*

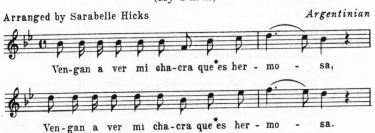

Ven-gan a ver mi cha-cra que*es her - mo - sa,

Ven-gan a ver mi cha-cra que*es her - mo - sa.

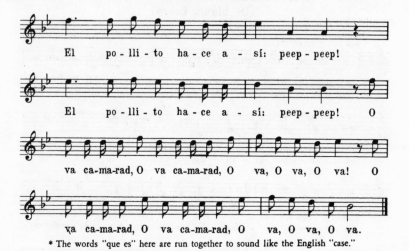

El po-lli-to ha-ce a-sí: peep-peep!

El po-lli-to ha-ce a-sí: peep-peep! O

va ca-ma-rad, O va ca-ma-rad, O va, O va, O va! O

va ca-ma-rad, O va ca-ma-rad, O va, O va, O va.

* The words "que es" here are run together to sound like the English "case."

El patito (*the duckling*) hace así: quack-quack!
El osito (*the little bear*) hace así: grr-grr!
El caballo (*the horse*) hace así: (neigh)
Y el burro (*and the donkey*) hace así: hee-haw!
Lechoncito (*piglet*) hace así: oink-oink!
El gatito (*the kitten*) hace así: miaow!
Lechucito (*owlet*) hace así: hoo-hoo!
Y el toro (*and the bull*) hace así: (roar)

Guide to Spanish pronunciation

a as in father

e as in grey

i (also y) as in machine

ch as in chance

ll is l followed by the consonant y

v is almost b, and vice versa

h is silent

qu is like k

    c before i and e is like s, in Spanish-American speech, but in Castillian is lisped (th as in thin) ; c before a and o and u is hard.

    d at the end of a stressed final syllable (as in *camarad'*) is very nearly the th in thin.

The words literally mean "Come and see my farm which is so beautiful. The little chicken goes like this: peep-peep! O go, my friend, O go, my friend, etc." All verses are the same except that a different animal is chosen each time. The song is known in several South American countries and is sung also in Mexico.

The above version was taught to Kathleen Cartwright by Phyllis Aden who brought it from Argentina. Used by permission.

MORING SONG
(Las Mañanitas)

English version by J.E.T.
Mexican

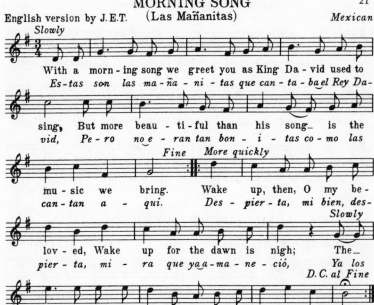

With a morn-ing song we greet you as King Da-vid used to
Es-tas son las ma-ña-ni-tas que can-ta-ba el Rey Da-

sing, But more beau-ti-ful than his song is the
vid, Pe-ro no e-ran tan bon-i-tas co-mo las

Fine More quickly

mu-sic we bring. Wake up, then, O my be-
can-tan a-qui. Des-pier-ta, mi bien, des-

Slowly

lov-ed, Wake up for the dawn is nigh; The
pier-ta, mi-ra que ya a-ma-ne-ció, Ya los

D.C. al Fine

birds are sweet-ly sing-ing, The moon has gone from the sky.
pa-ja-ri-llos can-tan, la lu-na ya se me-tió.

The above is a fine example of a folk aubade, a song sung at dawn. It is often used as a birthday morning greeting.

Contributed by Mrs. de Villasante and Mrs. Milton Lancelot of Mexico City,

LITTLE SWEET ONE
(La Chaparrita)

English version by J.E.T.
Mexican

Good - bye, my lit-tle sweet one,____
From the low-lands he will bring you____

____Don't cry now for your Pan-cho,____ For when he leaves the
____ A kiss, a pret-ty treas-ure,____ A trin-ket for your

ranch - o____ He'll soon come back a - gain.
pleas - ure____ So you'll for-get your pain.

For your hair a bow be - witch - ing, _____ A shawl with fan-cy

stitch - ing _____ I'll give your ma - ma - ci - ta _____

_____ And a cot - ton pet - ti - coat.   MY, OH,   MY!

MY TWENTY PENNIES

Translated by J. Olcutt Sanders   *Venezuelan*

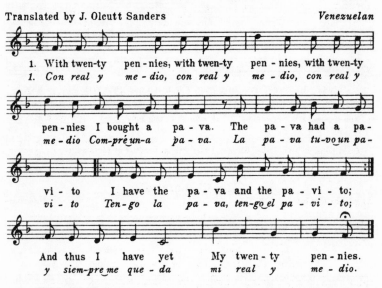

1. With twen-ty   pen - nies, with twen-ty   pen - nies, with twen-ty
1. *Con real y   me - dio, con real y   me - dio, con real y*

pen - nies I bought a   pa - va.   The   pa - va had a   pa-
me - dio Com-pré un-a   pa - va.   La   pa - va tu-vo un pa-

vi - to   I have the   pa - va and the pa - vi - to;
vi - to   Ten-go   la   pa - va, ten-go el pa - vi - to;

And thus I   have   yet   My twen - ty   pen - nies.
y   siem-pre me que - da   mi   real y   me - dio.

* Repeat in each stanza after the first, with all previous animals.
  (Pava turkey, pavito: baby turkey.)
2. Gata, (cat) gatito.   4. Mona, (monkey) monito.
3. Chiva, (goat) chivito.   5. Lora, (parrot) lorito.
                                          6. Vaca, (cow) vaquito.

By permission of the Cooperative Recreation Service, Delaware, Ohio.

WALKING AT NIGHT

English version by A.D.Z.   *Czech*

Strolling along

1. Walk - ing at night a - long the mea-dow way,

Home from the dance be - side my maid - en gay,

Walk - ing at night a - long the mea-dow way

Home from the dance be - side my maid - en gay. *Hey!

Chorus
Much faster. f second time pp

**Sto - do - le, sto - do - le, sto-do - le, pum - pa,

Sto-do-le, pum-pa, sto-do-le pum-pa, Sto-do-le, sto-do-le,

sto-do-le, pum-pa, Sto-do-le, pum-pa, pum, pum, pum.

2. Nearing the woods we heard the nightingale,
   Sweetly it helped me tell my begging tale.

3. Many the stars that brightly shone above,
   But none so bright as her one word of love.

*A merry shout. **"Stodole" means barn and "pumpa" pump. The words here are simply used to make a gay chorus. The song was made known in this country by Mrs. Stella Marek Cushing.

From "Singing America." Used by permission of the National Recreation Association, owners of the copyright, and C. C. Birchard and Co., publishers.

TWANKYDILLO

English. Sussex

1. Here's a health to the jol-ly black-smith, the best of all fel-lows, Who works at his an-vil while the boy blows the

Chorus

bel-lows; Which makes my bright ham-mer to rise and to fall, Here's to old Cole, and to young Cole, and to old Cole of all. Twan-ky - dil - lo, Twan-ky - dil - lo, Twan-ky - dil- lo, dil- lo, dil- lo, dil - lo, A roar-ing pair of *bag-pipes made of the green wil-low.

2. If a gentleman calls his horse for to shoe,
   He makes no denial of one pot or two,
   For it makes my bright hammer to rise, etc.

3. Here's a health to King Charlie and also his queen,
   And to all the royal little ones wher'er they are seen,
   Which makes my bright hammer to rise, etc.

*"Bagpipes" here means "blowpipes."

DON'T WANT TO GO HOME

English version by F. H. *Czech*

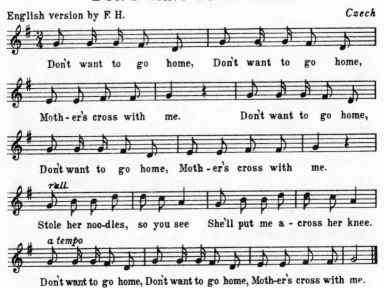

Don't want to go home, Don't want to go home,

Moth-er's cross with me. Don't want to go home,

Don't want to go home, Moth-er's cross with me.

rall.

Stole her noo-dles, so you see She'll put me a-cross her knee.

a tempo

Don't want to go home, Don't want to go home, Moth-er's cross with me.

Contributed by Fjeril Hess.

JOHNNY HAS GONE FOR A SOLDIER

U. S. War of Independence

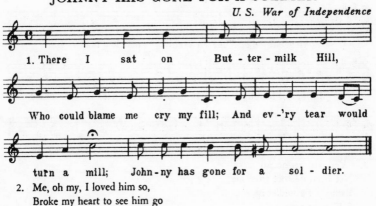

1. There I sat on But-ter-milk Hill,

Who could blame me cry my fill; And ev-'ry tear would

turn a mill; John-ny has gone for a sol-dier.

2. Me, oh my, I loved him so,
Broke my heart to see him go
And only time will heal my woe;
Johnny has gone for a soldier.

From the collection of John Allison. Used by permission. Available on Victor record 26460-B.

CHERRIES ARE RIPE

U. S.

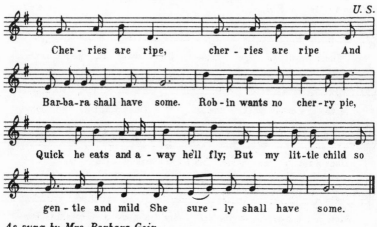

Cher - ries are ripe, cher - ries are ripe And Bar-ba-ra shall have some. Rob-in wants no cher-ry pie, Quick he eats and a - way he'll fly; But my lit-tle child so gen - tle and mild She sure - ly shall have some.

As sung by Mrs. Barbara Goin

TO THE GARDEN ANNIE WENT

With a dance rhythm   *Bohemian*

1. To the gar-den An-nie went, An-nie went, An-nie went, Cut-ting cab-bage her in - tent, her in - ten - tion. Jo - ey fol-lowed bent on fun. Scat-tered all that she had done, "Oh! oh! oh! naugh-ty Joe! Pay for this be - fore you go."

2. "You will get no pay from me,
Not from me, not from me;
Rather I'd a soldier be,
Soldier become."
"Don't be such a wicked lad,
That would make your parents sad;
No! no! no! naughty Joe!
Pay for this before you go."

From "Twenty Two Bohemian Folk Songs," by the Reverend Vincent Pisek, D.D. Used by permmission of the Jan Hus Presbyterian Church, N. Y. City.

GREETING SONG

Three Part Canon

CALDARA 1670-1736

Wel - come, here's to you!

We're glad to have you with us here to - day;

This may be sung as a two or three part canon, the second and third voices entering when the preceding voice has reached the asterisk. It may be sung as often as required in strict tempo, but should end on the word "you"! The first and second voices hold this note till the third voice "catches them up" so that all the singers finish together.

THE RED HERRING

1st and 2nd voices   *English*

1. What d'ye think I have made with my red her-ring's head? As

jol - ly an o - ven as ev - er baked bread. O - ven, bread, and

ev - er - y thing And I think I've done well with my

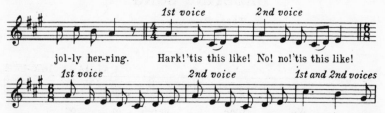

jol-ly her-ring. Hark!'tis this like! No! no!'tis this like!

Why did-n't you tell me so? So I did long a-go. Well! Well! and

ev-er-y-thing, And I think I've done well with my jol-ly her-ring!

2. What d'ye think I have made with my red herring's eyes?
   As jolly old saucers as ever baked pies. Saucers, pies, and everything,
   And I think I've done well with my jolly herring.
       Hark! 'tis this like! etc.

3. What d'ye think I have made with my red herring's tail?
   As jolly a ship as ever set sail. Ship, sail, and everything,
   And I think I've done well with my jolly herring.
       Hark! 'tis this like! etc.

4. What d'ye think I have made with my red herring's ribs?
   Why! forty new cradles and fifty new cribs. Cradles, cribs, and everything,
   And I think I've done well with my jolly herring.
       Hark! 'tis this like! etc.

5. What d'ye think I have made with my herring's backbone?
   As jolly a chopper as ever chopped stone. Chopper, stone, and everything,
   And I think I've done well with my jolly herring.
       Hark! 'tis this like! etc.

6. What d'ye think I have made with my red herring's back?
   As jolly a hackney as carried a sack. Hackney, sack, and everything,
   And I think I've done well with my jolly herring.
       Hark! 'tis this like! etc.

7. What d'ye think I have made with my fish as a whole?
   As jolly a wagon as ever hauled coal. Wagon, coal, and everything,
   And I think I've done well with my jolly herring.
       Hark! 'tis this like! etc.

MAY SONG

Translated by C.C.   *German*

How won-der-ful_ is May-time With flow-ers in
bloom ev-'ry - where,__ I would that my_ be - lov -
ed Were here my joy__ to share;__ If she with
me__would stay__ In all the splen-dor of
May - time My heart would be hap - py and gay.__

Descant optional for repetition of song

How won - der - ful__ is May - time With
I would that my__ be - lov - ed Were

flow-ers in bloom ev-'ry where,   If she with me__would
here__ my joy__ to share;

stay__ In all the splen-dor of May -

time my heart would be hap-py and gay.__

Contributed by Charlotte Carlin.

LUSTUKRU

English version by J.E.T.   *French. Brittany*

1. From the plain there comes a creak-ing sound That chills us to the bone.___ Do you hear it? Like the gra-ting of a chain dragged o-ver stone.___ For it's old Lus-tu-kru who's pass-ing, Comes and goes with step a-creep, And he'll pop in-to his bas-ket All the lit-tle chil-dren not a-sleep. Lon lon la, lon lon la,

1st verse   *2nd verse*

lon lon la, Li-re la lon la.   la lon la.

2. Now you ask me have I anyone
   To add to his supplies.
   Not my Johnnie or my Janie,
   They have tightly closed their eyes.
   Go away, Lustukru, go elsewhere,
   Ugly man with step a-creep!
   For I've no one for your basket,
   Both my little children are fast asleep.
   Lon lon la, etc.

THE FORGE

English version by J.E.T.

JOHANNES BRAHMS
(1833-1897)

Measured, and in moderate time

The black-smith I hear, The clang-ing and
How strong is his stroke, The sparks up-ward

clash-ing, His ham-mer blows flash-ing On
go-ing, The bel-lows he's blow-ing, The

an-vil are crash-ing, Their rhym-ing and
furn-ace •is glow-ing, A Thor with his

chim-ing fall loud_____ on the ear.
thun-der he stands_____ in the smoke.

WHITE CORAL BELLS
Two Part Canon

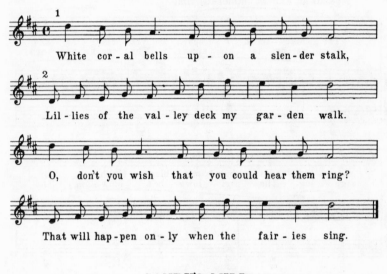

1 White cor-al bells up-on a slen-der stalk,

2 Lil-lies of the val-ley deck my gar-den walk.

O, don't you wish that you could hear them ring?

That will hap-pen on-ly when the fair-ies sing.

SANDY'S MILL
Two Part Canon

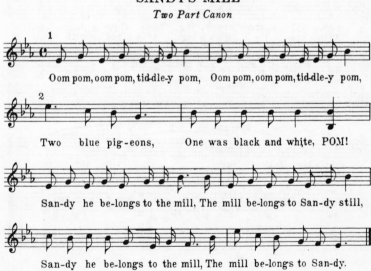

1 Oom pom, oom pom, tid-dle-y pom, Oom pom, oom pom, tid-dle-y pom,

2 Two blue pig-eons, One was black and white, POM!

San-dy he be-longs to the mill, The mill be-longs to San-dy still,

San-dy he be-longs to the mill, The mill be-longs to San-dy.

THE CLOCKS
Three Part Round

Danish

Sto - re u - re si - ger tick, tock, tick, tock, Min-dre
*Sto - re oo-re see-er Min-dre

u - re si - ger tick-a, tock-a, tick-a, tock-a, Lom - me
oo-re see-er Lō - me

u - re si - ger tick-ie, tick-ie, tick-ie, tick-ie, tick-ie, tick-ie, tick.
oo-re see-er

*Approximate pronunciation in English. The words mean:—

Big clocks say tick, tock, etc.
Small clocks say ticka, tocka, etc.
Watches say tickie, tickie, etc.

Contributed by Mr. and Mrs. Werner B. Johnson.

GRASSHOPPERS THREE
Three Part Round

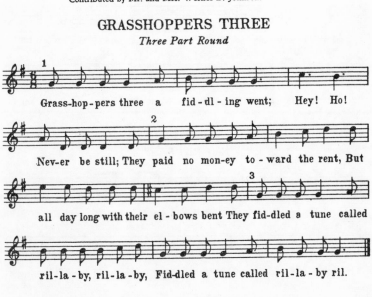

Grass-hop-pers three a fid - dl - ing went; Hey! Ho!

Nev-er be still; They paid no mon-ey to - ward the rent, But

all day long with their el - bows bent They fid-dled a tune called

ril-la - by, ril-la - by, Fid-dled a tune called ril-la - by ril.

JUNE, LOVELY JUNE
Three Part Canon

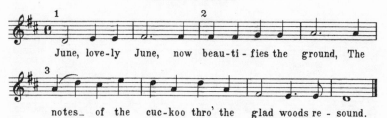

June, love-ly June, now beau-ti-fies the ground, The

notes— of the cuc-koo thro' the glad woods re-sound.

DONA NOBIS PACEM
Three Part Round

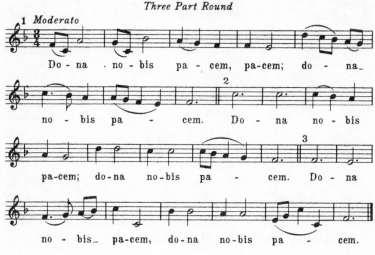

Do - na - no - bis pa - cem, pa-cem; do - na—

no - bis pa - cem. Do - na no - bis

pa-cem; do-na no-bis pa - cem. Do - na

no - bis— pa-cem, do-na no-bis pa - cem.

MAKE NEW FRIENDS
Four Part Round

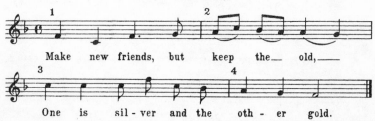

Make new friends, but keep the— old,—

One is sil-ver and the oth-er gold.

THE SWAN SINGS
Four Part Round

The swan sings teer-i-li-o   teer-i-li-o   teer-i-li-o.

This also sounds well as a three part canon. End on a chord with all voices singing a sustained "O."

WHIP-POOR-WILL
Three Part Round

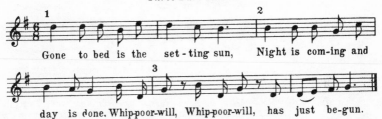

Gone to bed is the set-ting sun, Night is com-ing and

day is done. Whip-poor-will, Whip-poor-will, has just be-gun.

THE CROW-FISH MAN

U. S. Kentucky

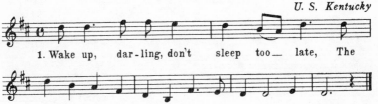

1. Wake up, dar-ling, don't sleep too— late, The

crow-fish man's done past our gate This morn-ing so soon.

2. Selling crow-fish two for a dime,
   Nobody's crow-fish eats like mine,
   This morning so soon.

3. All 'round the mountain I must go,
   If anything happens let me know,
   This morning so soon.

4. Come to my house, just come to the field;
   If you can't bring the money, bring meat and meal,
   This morning so soon.

From "Folk Songs of the Southern Appalachians" by Cecil Sharp. Used by permission of the Oxford University Press.

TWO WINGS

U. S. Negro Spiritual

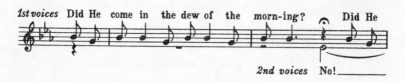

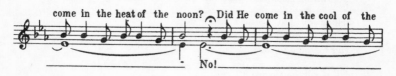

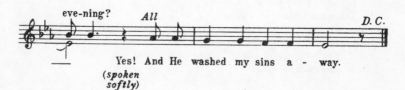

JENNIE JENKINS

U.S. W. Virginia
Sandy River Area

1st voices

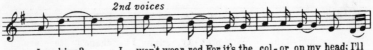

1. Will you wear red, my dear, O dear? O will you wear red, Jen-nie

2nd voices

Jen-kins?___ I won't wear red For it's the col-or on my head; I'll

buy me a blue gown, ruf-fy-tuf-fy, silk-y-jew-'lie,

All

tir-lie-whirl-ie O!___ Roll,___ Jen-nie Jen-kins, roll!

2. Will you wear white, my dear, O dear?
   O will you wear white, Jennie Jenkins?
   I won't wear white
   For the color's too bright;
   I'll buy me, etc.

3. Will you wear black, my dear, O dear?
   O will you wear black, Jennie Jenkins?
   I won't wear black
   For it's the color on my back;
   I'll buy me, etc.

4. Will you wear pink, my dear, O dear?
   O will you wear pink, Jennie Jenkins?
   I won't wear pink
   For my love might sink;
   I'll buy me, etc.

5. Will you wear green, my dear, O dear?
   O will you wear green, Jennie Jenkins?
   I won't wear green
   For it's a shame to be seen;
   I'll buy me, etc.

As sung by Mr. James Norris.

SACRAMENTO

U. S. Shanty

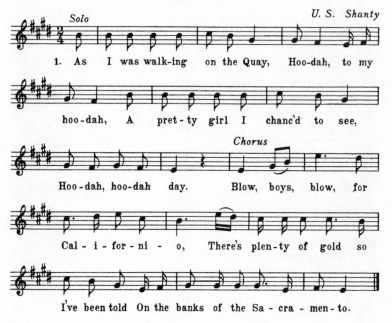

1. As I was walk-ing on the Quay, Hoo-dah, to my hoo-dah, A pret-ty girl I chanc'd to see, Hoo-dah, hoo-dah day. Blow, boys, blow, for Cal-i-for-ni-o, There's plen-ty of gold so I've been told On the banks of the Sa-cra-men-to.

2. Her hair was brown, her eyes were blue,
   Her lips were red and sweet to view.

3. I raised my hat and said, "How do?"
   She bowed and said, "Quite well, thank you."

4. I asked her then to come with me
   Down to the docks my ship to see.

5. She quickly answered, "Oh dear no,
   I thank you, but I cannot go."

6. "I have a sweetheart young and true,
   And cannot give my heart to you."

7. I said, "Good-bye" and strode away,
   Although with her I longed to stay.

8. And as I bade this girl adieu
   I said that girls like her were few.

OUT IN OUR MEADOW
(Uti vår hage)

Translated by Per G. Stensland
Columbia University

*Swedish
Medieval Gotland*

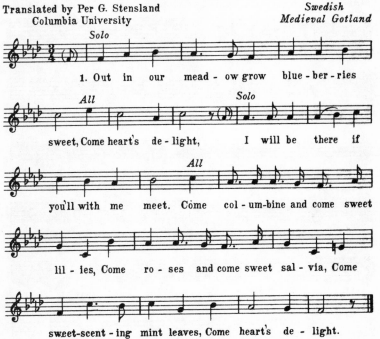

1. Out in our mead-ow grow blue-ber-ries sweet, Come heart's de-light, I will be there if you'll with me meet. Come col-um-bine and come sweet lil-ies, Come ro-ses and come sweet sal-via, Come sweet-scent-ing mint leaves, Come heart's de-light.

2. Beautiful flowers are dancing so light, ·
   Come heart's delight,
   I'll bind a wreath to my lover's delight.
   Come columbine, etc.

3. The wreath I shall put 'round your light golden hair.
   Come heart's delight,
   The sun sets in darkness but hope rises fair.
   Come columbine, etc.

4. Out in our meadow grow flowers and fruits.
   Come heart's delight.
   You are the flower that my own heart suits.
   Come columbine, etc.

Used by permission.

LA BIRITULLERA

Paraphrase by J. E. T.

Italian

1. Oh, come to me sweet-heart, my dear - est one, Oh,
come and walk with me, do! On - ly you can con -
sole my heart's heav - i - ness, I want to talk with you.

Chorus

Yes, with you beau - ti - ful Bi - ri bi - ri bi - ri
tul - le - ra, tul - le - ra, tul - le - ra lal - le - ral -
le - ra, Yes, with you beau - ti - ful Bi - ri bi - ri bi - ri
tul - le - ra, tul - le - ra, tul - le - ra lal - le - ra là!____

2. They tell me you sing sweetest roundelays
   With voice so graceful and free.
   Only you can console my heart's heaviness,
   So come and sing with me.
   Yes, with me, etc.

3. Oh, let us make merry, my dearest one,
   And join in gay revelry.
   Only you can console my heart's heaviness,
   So come and laugh with me.
   Yes, with me, etc.

A FOX WENT OUT ONE STARRY NIGHT

English

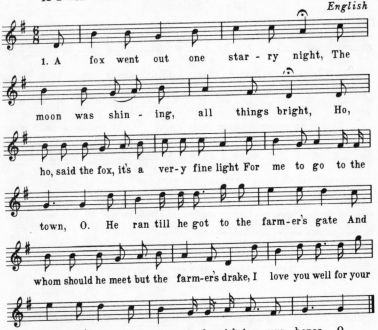

1. A fox went out one star-ry night, The
moon was shin-ing, all things bright, Ho,
ho, said the fox, it's a ver-y fine light For me to go to the
town, O. He ran till he got to the farm-er's gate And
whom should he meet but the farm-er's drake, I love you well for your
mas-ter's sake And long to be pick-ing your bones, O.

2. The gray goose she ran all around the hay-stack,
   Ho, ho, said the fox, you are very fat,
   You'll grease my bones and you'll ride on my back
   From this to yonder town, O.
   The farmer's wife she jumped out of bed
   And out of the window she popped her head,
   Oh, farmer, oh, farmer, the geese are all dead,
   For the fox has been to the town, O.

3. The farmer he loaded his pistol with lead
   And shot the old fox right through the head,
   Ho, ho, said the farmer, I think you're quite dead,
   And you'll no more trouble my town, O.
   The farmer's wife took the fox's skin
   And on to it sewed her Sunday pin,
   Ho, ho, said the farmer, a very fine thing
   For you to wear to the town, O.

This song, of which there are many variants in the British Isles and the U. S., dates back to 1492. Compare the tune with "The Keel Row."

CHRISTMAS POLKA
(Nu är det Jul igen)

English version by J. E. T.

Swedish

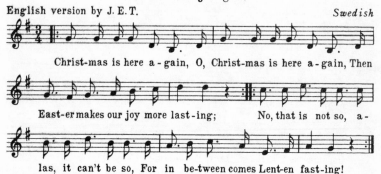

Christ-mas is here a-gain, O, Christ-mas is here a-gain, Then

East-er makes our joy more last-ing;   No, that is not so, a-

las, it can't be so, For in be-tween comes Lent-en fast-ing!

No Swedish Christmas is complete without the above tune to which people dance in a long line through the rooms of their houses ending around the tree. All hold hands and in time with the music proceed in processional formation taking one heavy step, followed by two light ones, starting alternately with the right and left feet.

MY LORD, WHAT A MORNIN'!

Chorus

U. S. Negro Spiritual

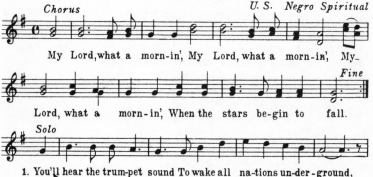

My Lord, what a morn-in', My Lord, what a morn-in', My

Fine

Lord, what a morn-in', When the stars be-gin to fall.

Solo

1. You'll hear the trum-pet sound To wake all na-tions un-der-ground,

Chorus

D. C.

Look-in' to my God's right hand, When the stars be-gin to fall.

2. You'll hear the sinners moan
   To wake all nations, etc.

3. You'll hear the angels sing
   To wake all nations, etc.

THE FARMER AND THE CROW
(Bonden och kråkan)

Translated by Per G. Stensland
Columbia University

Swedish 15th Century

1. The farm-er he drove to the fir tree woods,

Hey-om, fey-om, fal-ler-al-er-ah;____ Spied in a tree__ a

caw-ing crow, Hey-om, fey-om, fal-ler-al-er-ah.

2. Back to his house in a scare ran he,
   "Ma, that crow's a-biting me!"

3. Ma she sat down in her chair to sew,
   Saying, "Nobody heard of a man-bitin' crow!"

4. The farmer he then put his bow to his knee,
   And down came the crow from the highest tree.

5. That crow he brought home, and how crazy it sounds,
   The fat went to candles, well fifteen pounds.

6. The wings they were made into fans so sweet,
   That the girls could use to keep from the heat.

7. The skins they were worked into twelve pair of shoes,
   And slippers for Ma to keep her from bruise.

8. The meat they were salting for days to come,
   Pa wanted pickles, and he got some.

9. The beak they did raise to a steeple high,
   The head was a vane to tell the wind by.

10. The rest of the crow made a big gallalee,
    Biggest you saw in the Kattegat sea.

THE BIRD SONG

U. S. *Appalachian*

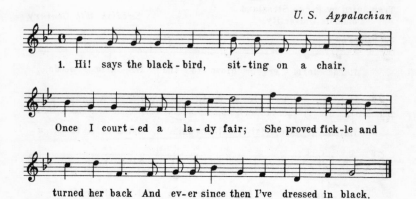

1. Hi! says the black-bird, sit-ting on a chair,
Once I court-ed a la-dy fair; She proved fick-le and
turned her back And ev-er since then I've dressed in black.

2. Hi! says the blue jay as she flew,
   If I was a young man I'd have two;
   If one proved fickle and chanced for to go,
   I'd have a new string to my bow.

3. Hi! says the little leather wingéd bat,
   I will tell you the reason that,
   The reason that I fly at night
   Is because I lost my heart's delight.

4. Hi! says the woodpecker, sitting on a fence,
   Once I courted a handsome wench,
   She proved fickle and from me fled,
   And ever since then my head's been red.

5. Hi! says the hawk unto the crow,
   If you ain't black then I don't know,
   Ever since old Adam was born
   You've been accused of stealing corn.

6. Hi! says the robin with a little squirm,
   I wish I had a great big worm;
   I would fly away into my nest,
   I have a wife I think the best.

THE ROBIN'S LAST WILL

English

At an easy pace

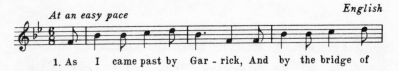

1. As I came past by Gar - rick, And by the bridge of

Dee, I saw a lit - tle Rob - bin __ Sit - ting on a

Chorus

tree. Too-ra - loo, Too-ra - loo, Too-ra - loo, ra-too-ra - loo. __

2. I said, "My pretty Robin,
   How long have you sat here?"
   He said, "I've lived upon this tree
   These four and twenty year." Too-ra-loo, etc.

3. "I'm going to make my testament
   Just here upon this tree,
   I'm going to make my testament
   This day before I dee." Too-ra-loo, etc.

4. "I'll give my pretty head,
   It is both round and small,
   Unto the boys of Garrick
   To play at the football." Too-ra-loo, etc.

5. "I'll give my pretty legs,
   They are both slim and tall
   Unto the bridge of Garrick,
   I hear it's going to fall." Too-ra-loo, etc.

6. As little Robin ended
   He shut his pretty eyes,
   And down he dropped unto the ground
   Never more to rise. Too-ra-loo, etc.

The chorus should reflect the feeling of each preceding verse.

WE'LL ALL GO DOWN THE MEADOW

British

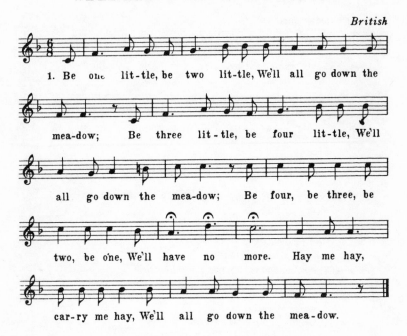

1. Be one lit-tle, be two lit-tle, We'll all go down the mea-dow; Be three lit-tle, be four lit-tle, We'll all go down the mea-dow; Be four, be three, be two, be one, We'll have no more. Hay me hay, car-ry me hay, We'll all go down the mea-dow.

2. Be five little, be six little, we'll all go down the meadow;
   Be seven little, be eight little, we'll all go down the meadow;
   Be eight, be seven, be six, be five, be four, be three, be two, be one,
   We'll have no more.
   Hay me hay, carry me hay,
   We'll all go down the meadow.

3. Be nine little, etc.

4. Be thirteen little, etc.

5. Be seventeen little, etc.

This song should be sung with very deliberate rhythm. Harmony on the sentence "We'll have no more" makes an effective variation.

Contributed by Gwladys Davies.

WAYFARING STRANGER

U. S. White Spiritual

I'm just a poor way-far-ing stran-ger, A - trav'ling
through this world of woe; But there's no
sick - ness, toil nor dan-ger In that bright world to which I
go I'm go-ing there to see my { fa - ther, / moth-er, / sis - ter, / broth-er, } I'm go-ing
there no more to roam, I'm on-ly go - ing o-ver
Jor-dan, I'm on - ly go - ing o-ver home.

SONG OF THE MAREMMA

English version by A. W. and J. E. T.   *Italian*

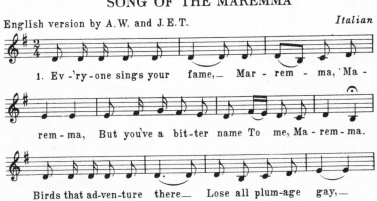

1. Ev -'ry-one sings your fame,— Mar - rem - ma, Ma -
rem - ma, But you've a bit-ter name To me, Ma - rem - ma.
Birds that ad-ven-ture there— Lose all plum-age gay,—

Young men who breathe its air Love must cast a - way.

2. If to that vale you go
   There'll be no returning,
   Heavy my heart with woe
   Ever will be yearning.
   Cursed be your beauty rare,
   Valley all a-bloom,
   Cursed be the men you lure
   Our love to doom.

The Maremma is a fertile valley in Tuscany; the women curse its beauty because the men who work there die of malaria.

Collected in Grosetto by Alice White, American Red Cross.

THE NIGHTINGALE

Translated by C. C.   *German Minnesinger*

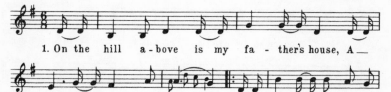

1. On the hill a - bove is my fa - ther's house, A __

lin-den in bloom stands near, __ There - in is __ sing-ing a

night - in - gale In tunes so bright and clear. __

2. O nightingale, sweet little bird,
   If thou teachest me thy singing
   Around thy feet, around thy neck
   Silver and gold shall be jingling.

3. I do not care for silver and gold,
   Such splendor never bound me;
   I am only a little bird of the woods
   As free as the air around me.

If so desired a few voices may sing the small upper notes, care being taken not to sub merge the melody.

Contributed by Charlotte Carlin.

AS I ROLL MY ROLLING BALL

Paraphrase by J. E. T.   *French - Canadian*

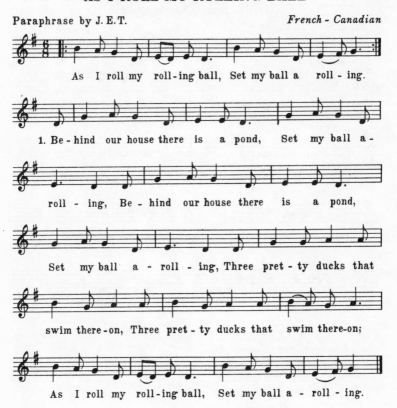

As I roll my roll-ing ball, Set my ball a roll - ing.

1. Be - hind our house there is a pond, Set my ball a -

roll - ing, Be - hind our house there is a pond,

Set my ball a - roll - ing, Three pret - ty ducks that

swim there-on, Three pret - ty ducks that swim there-on;

As I roll my roll-ing ball, Set my ball a - roll - ing.

2. A passing prince a-hunting bound,
   The black he saw, the white he downed.

3. O prince, that was a cruel thing,
   A mortal wound beneath her wing.

4. The feathers fly into the air,
   Are gathered by three ladies fair.

5. They make a camp-fire soft and deep,
   So passers-by may soundly sleep.

If so desired a soloist may sing the narrative lines.

WILLIE, TAKE YOUR LITTLE DRUM
(Guillô, prends ton tambourin)

Bernard de la Monnoye
(1641-1728)
English version by J. E. T.

French Carol
Early Burgundian

Gaily

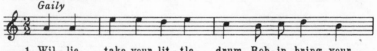

1. Wil - lie, take your lit - tle drum, Rob - in, bring your

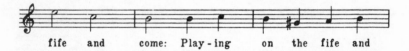

fife and come: Play - ing on the fife and

drum, Tu - re - lu - re - lu, pat - a - pat - a - pan, We'll make

mu - sic loud and gay For our Christ - mas hol - i - day.

2. Shepherds glad in ancient days
   Gave the King of Kings their praise,
   Playing on the fife and drum,
   Tu-ru-lu-re-lu, pat-a-pat-a-pan,
   They made music loud and gay
   On the Holy Child's birthday.

3. Christian men, rejoice as one,
   Leave your work and join our fun;
   Playing on the fife and drum,
   Tu-ru-lu-re-lu, pat-a-pat-a-pan,
   We'll make music loud and gay
   For our Christmas holiday.

Carol, used to mean a ring-dance with singing and dancing, was a part of early religious ceremonies. The above song has a dance-like rhythm.

MY HOME'S IN MONTANA

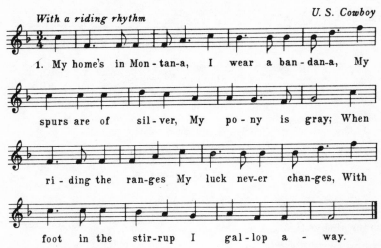

With a riding rhythm U. S. Cowboy

1. My home's in Mon-tan-a, I wear a ban-dan-a, My spurs are of sil-ver, My po-ny is gray; When ri-ding the ran-ges My luck nev-er chan-ges, With foot in the stir-rup I gal-lop a-way.

2. When far from the ranches
I cut the pine branches
To lay out a bed
When the starlight is pale;

When I have partaken
Of beans and of bacon
I whistle a merry old
Song of the trail.

The words for "My Home's in Montana" are taken from *Blending Voices* of *The World of Music* series, 1936, and are used with the permission of Ginn & Company, owners of the copyright.

GRANDMA GRUNTS

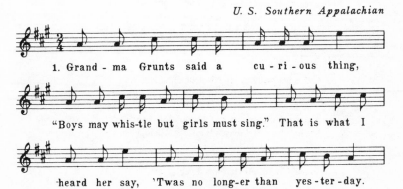

U. S. Southern Appalachian

1. Grand-ma Grunts said a cu-ri-ous thing, "Boys may whis-tle but girls must sing." That is what I heard her say, 'Twas no long-er than yes-ter-day.

Boys can whis-tle   (*whistle*)   Girls must sing Tra-la-la-la-la.

2. Boys can whistle, of course, they may,
    They can whistle the livelong day.
    Why can't girls whistle too, pray tell,
    If they manage to do it well?

3. Grandma Grunts said it wouldn't do,
    Gave a very good reason too:
    Whistling girls and crowing hens
    Always come to some bad ends.

FROM SKY ABOVE

Translated by C. C.   *German carol*

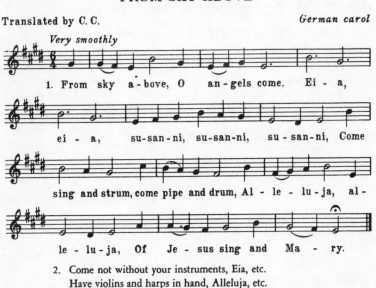

1. From sky a-bove, O an-gels come.   Ei - a,
ei - a,   su-san-ni, su-san-ni, su - san - ni, Come
sing and strum, come pipe and drum, Al - le - lu - ja, al -
le - lu - ja, Of Je - sus sing and Ma - ry.

2. Come not without your instruments, Eia, etc.
    Have violins and harps in hand, Alleluja, etc.

3. The voice of the lute should sound soft and sweet, Eia, etc.
    So that the Child may fall asleep, Alleluja, etc.

4. On earth be peace, fraternity, Eia, etc.
    Praise God in all eternity, Alleluja, etc.

Contributed by Charlotte Carlin.

SOFT FALLS THE DEW

English version by F. H.   *Slovak*

Smoothly, do not drag

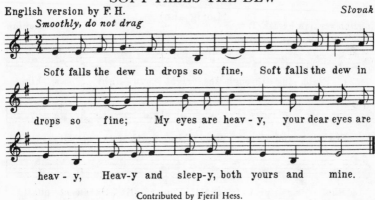

Soft falls the dew in drops so fine, Soft falls the dew in drops so fine; My eyes are heav-y, your dear eyes are heav-y, Heav-y and sleep-y, both yours and mine.

Contributed by Fjeril Hess.

WHERE ARE YOU GOING TO, MY PRETTY MAID?

English

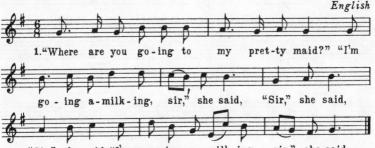

1."Where are you go-ing to my pret-ty maid?" "I'm go-ing a-milk-ing, sir," she said, "Sir," she said, "Sir," she said, "I'm go-ing a-milk-ing, sir," she said.

2. "May I go with you, my pretty maid?"
"You're kindly welcome, sir," she said,
"Sir," she said, "Sir," she said,
"Your're kindly welcome, sir," she said.

3. "What is your father, my pretty maid?"
• "My father's a farmer, sir," she said, etc.

4. "Say, will you marry me, my pretty maid?"
"Yes, if you please, kind sir," she said, etc.

5. "What is your fortune, my pretty maid?"
"My face is my fortune, sir," she said, etc.

6. "Then I won't marry you, my pretty maid."
"Nobody asked you, sir," she said, etc.

For suggestions on the dramatizing of this song see "Dramatized Ballads" by Janet E. Tobitt and Alice M. G. White, published by E. P. Dutton and Company, Inc.

THE QUAIL
(Lorigjahn)

English version by J. E. T.

Armenian

Rather fast, spirited

1. Flash-ing through the bright sun-light I saw him,

Scar-let and green shone his feath-ers so clear;

Such a pret-ty quail, dear lit-tle sweet quail,

Though I called he would not— hear,

Though I called he would not— hear.

Chorus

Lu-li, lu-li, lu-li, lu-li, quail so pret-ty,

quail so pret-ty, quail so love-ly, Lu-li, lu-li, lu-li, lu-li,

quail so pret-ty, Green quail of my heart.

2. Let us mingle our voices together
   Singing as one with melody gay;
   Such a pretty quail, dear little sweet quail,
   Be my comrade on the way,
   Be my comrade on the way.

Contributed by Armené Dikijian.

SING ME YOUR SONG O!

I HAVE A SONG TO SING, O!

from

The Yeoman of the Guard

ARTHUR SULLIVAN
(1842-1900)

1. I have a song to sing, O! Sing me your song, O!_____ It is sung to the moon by a love lorn _ loon, Who fled from the mock - ing throng, O! It's the song of a mer - ry man mop - ing mum, Whose soul was sad and whose glance was glum, Who sipped no sup and he craved no crumb, As he sighed for the love of a la - dye.

I HAVE A SONG TO SING, O!

CHORUS (continued)

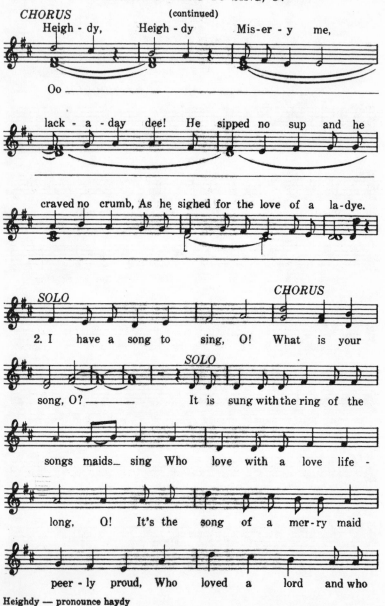

Heigh - dy, Heigh - dy Mis - er - y me,

Oo _____

lack - a - day dee! He sipped no sup and he

craved no crumb, As he sighed for the love of a la-dye.

SOLO **CHORUS**

2. I have a song to sing, O! What is your

SOLO

song, O? _____ It is sung with the ring of the

songs maids_ sing Who love with a love life -

long, O! It's the song of a mer-ry maid

peer - ly proud, Who loved a lord and who

Heighdy — pronounce haydy

(continued)

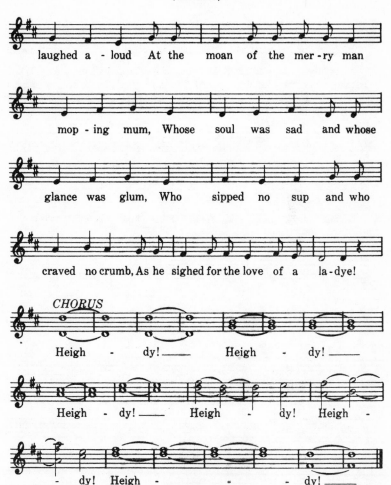

laughed a - loud At the moan of the mer-ry man

mop - ing mum, Whose soul was sad and whose

glance was glum, Who sipped no sup and who

craved no crumb, As he sighed for the love of a la-dye!

CHORUS

Heigh - dy! ___ Heigh - dy! ___

Heigh - dy! ___ Heigh - dy! Heigh -

- dy! Heigh - - dy! ___

This finale from "The Yeoman of the Guard" is sung by Jack Point, a jester, and Elsie Maynard, a strolling singer. Their solo parts may be taken by half the chorus and the alliterative words should be well enunciated.

JOLLY OLD ROGER

U.S. New England

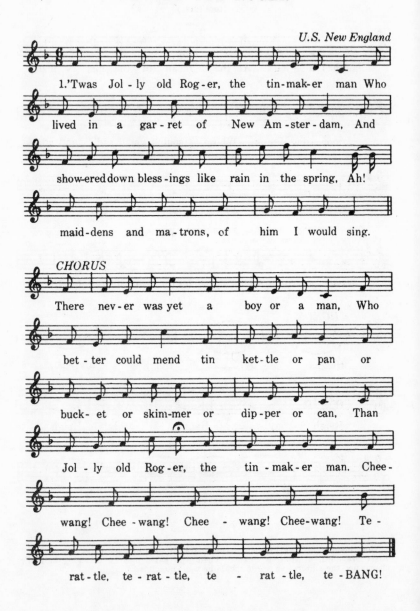

1.'Twas Jol - ly old Rog - er, the tin - mak - er man Who
lived in a gar - ret of New Am - ster - dam, And
show-ered down bless - ings like rain in the spring, Ah!
maid-dens and ma - trons, of him I would sing.

CHORUS

There nev - er was yet a boy or a man, Who
bet - ter could mend tin ket - tle or pan or
buck - et or skim-mer or dip - per or can, Than
Jol - ly old Rog - er, the tin - mak - er man. Chee -
wang! Chee - wang! Chee - wang! Chee-wang! Te -
rat - tle, te - rat - tle, te - rat - tle, te - BANG!

(continued)

2. Now Roger's bald pate was as smooth as your nose,
   And buying his stockings he purchased half-hose;
   He had but one leg and he wore but one shoe,
   And he stumped round his shop on a stiff timber toe.

The tin peddler was a favorite with New England housewives and their children alike; for the former he brought household necessities and bits of gossip, for the latter he often had a surprise gift in his pack. The chorus suggests the noisy rattle of his pots and pans.

From "Folk Songs of Old New England", by Eloise Hubbard Linscott, by permission of The Macmillan Company, publishers.

HONZA, I LOVE YOU

English version by J.E.T.

Czech

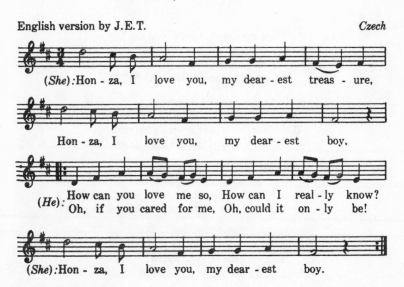

(She): Hon - za, I love you, my dear - est treas - ure,

Hon - za, I love you, my dear - est boy,

(He): How can you love me so, How can I real - ly know?
Oh, if you cared for me, Oh, could it on - ly be!

(She): Hon - za, I love you, my dear - est boy.

From "Naz Poklad". Bouquet of 270 Czechoslovakian Songs, by Ferdinand Sladek.

THERE WAS ONCE A LITTLE SHIP

Paraphrase by J.E.T.   *French*

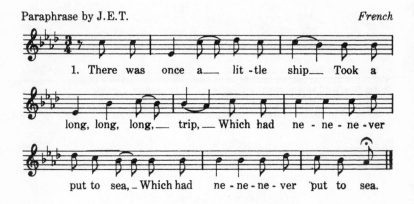

1. There was once a—— lit-tle ship—— Took a long, long, long,—— trip,—— Which had ne - ne - ne - ver put to sea, — Which had ne - ne - ne - ver put to sea.

2. When the crew's food would not last
   For a victim lots were cast;
   The poor ca-ca-cabin boy was "it",
   The poor ca-ca-cabin boy was "it".

3. To the heavens he made a plea
   That he might not eaten be —
   Neither fri-fri-fricasseed nor fried,
   Neither fri-fri-fricasseed nor fried.

4. As the cook made a fire hasty
   For that morsel young and tasty
   Fish by thou-thou-thousands jumped on deck!
   Fish by thou-thou-thousands jumped on deck!

5. So this timely visitation
   Saved a horrid situation;
   Shall we s-s-sing it all again?
   Shall we s-s-sing it all again?

The hesitation in the third and fourth lines is supposed to indicate the lurching of the ship.

SWIFTLY FLOWING LABE

Czech Marching Tune
Arr. by Fjeril Hess
and Lilian Jackson

1. A - bove a plain of gold and green A
young boy's head is plain - ly seen.

CHORUS

Hu - ya hu - ya hu - ya, ya, Swift - ly flow - ing
La - be, Hu - ya hu - ya
hu - ya, ya, Swift - ly flow - ing La - be.

2. But no, 'tis not his lifting head,
   'Tis Ifca's castle spires instead.

3. For our pleasure it was made,
   This gray old building deep in shade.

Labe — Elbe River

THE RAILROAD CORRAL

U.S. Cowboy

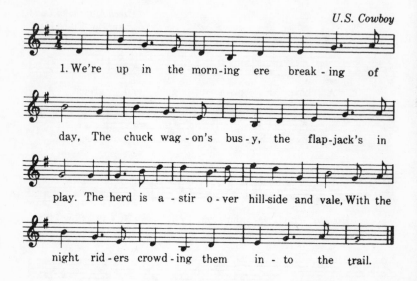

1. We're up in the morn-ing ere break-ing of day, The chuck wag-on's bus-y, the flap-jack's in play. The herd is a-stir o-ver hill-side and vale, With the night rid-ers crowd-ing them in-to the trail.

2. Come take up your cinches, come shake out your reins,
   Come wake your old bronco and break for the plains;
   Come roust out your steers from the long chaparral,
   For the outfit is off to the railroad corral.

3. The afternoon shadows are starting to lean
   When the chuck wagon sticks in the marshy ravine;
   The herds scatter farther than vision can look,
   You can bet all true punchers will help out the cook.

4. But the longest of days must reach evening at last,
   The hills all climbed, the creeks all past;
   The tired herd droops in the yellowing light —
   Let them droop if they will, for the Railroad's in sight!

   cinches — saddle girths   chaparral — thick scrub

This is considered one of the best cowboy songs; it should be sung with a light, galloping rhythm. Sometimes the herds take weeks to reach the railroad and the cowboys at night drive them a mile or two off the trail before bedding down so that they will not get mixed with other cattle in the darkness.

SPANISH LADIES

English
Capstan Shanty

1. Fare - well and a - dieu to— you Span - ish la - dies, Fare - well and a - dieu to you la - dies— of— Spain, For— we've re - ceived or - ders for to sail— for— old— Eng - land, But we hope— in a short time to see you a - gain.

CHORUS (*same tune as verses*)

    We'll rant and we'll roar like true British sailors,
    We'll rant and we'll roar across the salt seas
    Until we strike soundings in the Channel of Old England,
    From Ushant to Scilly is thirty-five leagues.

2. We hove our ship to when the wind was Sou'west, boys,
   We hove our ship to for to strike soundings clear;
   We got soundings in ninety-five fathom and boldly
   Up the Channel of Old England our courses we did steer.

3. Then the signal was made for the Grand Fleet to anchor,
   And all in the Downs that night for to lie;
   Then stand by your stoppers, let go your shank painters,
   Haul all your clew-garnets, let tacks and sheets fly.

stoppers — ropes for checking and holding chain cables
shank painters — securing ropes for anchors
haul all your clew-garnets — draw lower ends of sails to yard ready for furling
tacks and sheets — ropes at lower corner of sails for tautening them

THE LIFE THAT'S FREE

FLORENCE HOARE   *Alsatian*

1. I love the wild streams as they foam-ing leap With
thun-der-ing sounds o'er crag and steep, The
tu-mult, the glad-ness, The joy and the mad-ness O! it
fills my heart with glee,—— The tu-mult, the gladness, The
joy and the mad-ness, O! I love the life that's free.—

2. I love the red deer as it dashes by
   With quivering form and antlers high,
   The step of things fleeting,
   The throb of hearts beating,
   O! it fills my heart with glee.

3. I love the wild paths and the wildest song,
   The merriest things that to life belong,
   The breeze gaily blowing,
   The sea ever flowing,
   O! it fills my heart with glee.

By permission, from Curwen Edition No. 6268, published by J. Curwen and Sons, Ltd., 24 Berners Street, London, W. I. England.

67

HO! EVERY SLEEPER WAKEN

Three Part Round

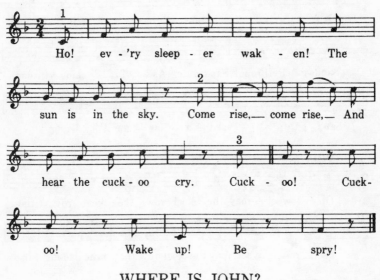

Ho! ev - 'ry sleep - er wak - en! The
sun is in the sky. Come rise,— come rise,— And
hear the cuck - oo cry. Cuck - oo! Cuck-
oo! Wake up! Be spry!

WHERE IS JOHN?

Three Part Round

From an air by
FRIEDRICH SMETANA
(1824-1884)

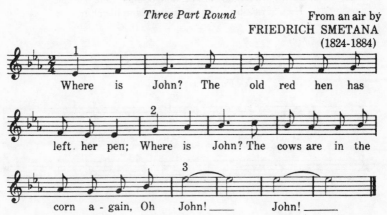

Where is John? The old red hen has
left her pen; Where is John? The cows are in the
corn a - gain, Oh John!___ John!___

From "The New Green Book," published by C. C. Birchard and Co., Boston, Mass.

THE KEEL ROW

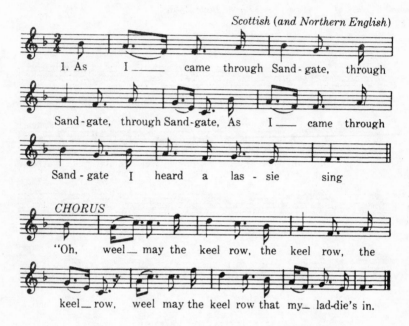

Scottish (and Northern English)

1. As I ___ came through Sand-gate, through Sand-gate, through Sand-gate, As I ___ came through Sand-gate I heard a las-sie sing

CHORUS

"Oh, weel ___ may the keel row, the keel row, the keel ___ row, weel may the keel row that my ___ lad-die's in.

2. He wears a blue bonnet, blue bonnet, blue bonnet,
   He wears a blue bonnet, a dimple in his chin.

PRAY GOD BLESS

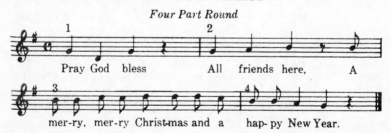

Four Part Round

1. Pray God bless 2. All friends here, A
3. mer-ry, mer-ry Christ-mas and a 4. hap-py New Year.

Contributed by Elizabeth Doubleday.

TURN AGAIN, WHITTINGTON

Three Part Round

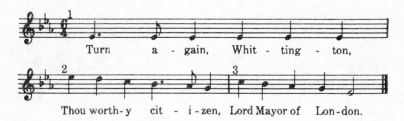

Turn a - gain, Whit - ting - ton,

Thou worth-y cit - i - zen, Lord Mayor of Lon-don.

AH, HOW THE MOON IS SHINING

Polish

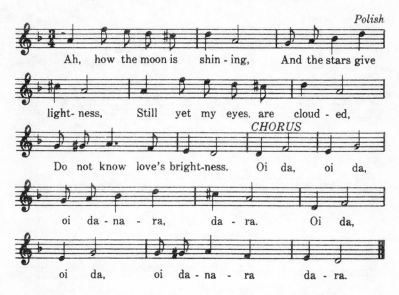

Ah, how the moon is shin - ing, And the stars give

light-ness, Still yet my eyes. are cloud-ed,

CHORUS

Do not know love's bright-ness. Oi da, oi da,

oi da - na - ra, da - ra. Oi da,

oi da, oi da - na - ra da - ra.

No, no. they're only feigning   Oh, if you want me, tell me,
  That they do not feel it,   For your love I'm aching,
Knowing—they're hesitating,   Oh, cease your cruel spurning,
  Dare not yet reveal it.   You're my poor heart breaking.

By the courtesy of Miss Jean Stewart.

From "The World Sings," by Janet E. Tobitt, published by The Year Book Press, London, England.

BEGONE, DULL CARE

English-17th Century

1. Be-gone, dull care!— I pri-thee be-gone— from me!— Be-gone, dull care! you and I — shall nev-er a - gree.— Long— time hast thou been tarry - ing here and fain thou would'st me kill,— But in faith, dull— care,— thou nev-er shalt have— thy will.—

2. Too much care will make a young man turn gray,
   And too much care will turn an old man into clay.
   My wife shall dance and I will sing, and merrily pass the day,
   For I hold it one of the wisest things to drive dull care away.

OH, WON'T YOU SIT DOWN?

Negro Camp-Meeting Song

CHORUS

1st group Oh, won't you sit down? *2nd group* Lawd, I can't sit down. Oh, won't you sit down? *1st group* Lawd, I can't sit down. Oh, won't you sit down? *1st group* Lawd, I can't sit down, 'Cause I just got to Hea-ven, Goin' to look a - round.

1. Who's that yon -der dressed in red? *2nd group* Must be the chil-dren that Mo - ses led.

1st group Who's that yon - der dressed in white? *2nd group* Must be the chil-dren of the Is - rael - ite.___

2. Who's that yonder dressed in blue?
   Must be the children that are comin' through.
   Who's that yonder dressed in black?
   Must be the hypocrites a-turnin' back.

THE BROOKLET

English version by J.E.T.   *Russian*

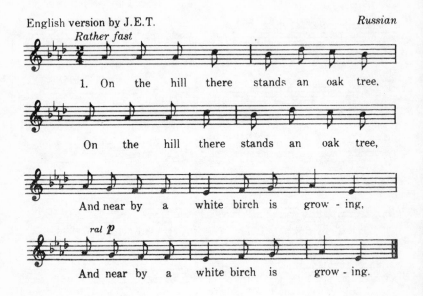

1. On the hill there stands an oak tree,
On the hill there stands an oak tree,
And near by a white birch is grow - ing,
And near by a white birch is grow - ing.

2. And between the birch and oak-tree,
   And between the birch and oak-tree
   Runs a little brooklet flowing,
   Runs a little brooklet flowing.

3. On through woods and on through meadows,
   On through woods and on through meadows,
   Leaps 'neath sun and soft breezes blowing,
   Leaps 'neath sun and soft breezes blowing.

4. Quickly speed thee to the river,
   Quickly speed thee to the river,
   None can stay thy restless going,
   None can stay thy restless going.

ALOUETTE

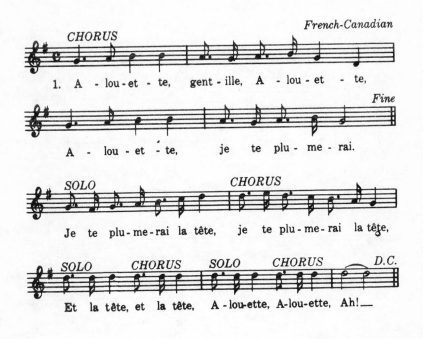

French-Canadian

CHORUS

1. A - lou - et - te, gent - ille, A - lou - et - te,

A - lou - et - te, je te plu - me - rai.

Fine

SOLO CHORUS

Je te plu - me - rai la tête, je te plu - me - rai la tête,

SOLO CHORUS SOLO CHORUS D.C.

Et la tête, et la tête, A - lou-ette, A-lou-ette, Ah!

2. Je te plumerai le bec, je te plumerai le bec,
   Et le bec, et le bec,
   Et la tête, et la tête,
   Alouette, Alouette, Ah!

3. Je te plumerai le nez. etc.

4. Je te plumerai les pattes. etc.

5. Je te plumerai le dos. etc.

6. Je te plumerai le cou. etc.

This is a cumulative song; as it proceeds the third measure from the end is repeated to include all the parts of the bird mentioned in the foregoing verses in reversed order.

THE ERIE CANAL

U.S. Work Song

1. I've got a mule her name is Sal, Fif-teen years on the E - rie Can - al. She's a good old work - er and a good old pal, Fif - teen years— on the E - rie Can - al.— We've hauled some barg -es in our day Filled with lum -ber, coal and hay, And ev-'ry inch of the way we know From Al - ba - ny— to— Buf - fa - lo.——

CHORUS

Low bridge, ev - 'ry - bod - y down! Low bridge, for we're go - in' through a town! And you'll al-ways know your neighbor, You'll al-ways know your pal, If you've ev - er nav - i - gat - ed on the E - rie Can - al.

2. We'd better get along, old gal,
   Fifteen years on the Erie Canal.
   You can bet your life I'd never part with Sal,
   Fifteen years on the Erie Canal.
   Git up there, mule, here comes a lock,
   We'll make Rome 'bout six o'clock;
   Just one more trip, and then we'll go,
   Right back home to Buffalo.

THE SHAMROCK AND THE HEATHER

J.E.T.   *Irish*

O the shamrock and the heather we

love full dear, And the dew on the

grass-land when the sun's shining clear.

The lakes and the loughs with their silver sheen Are

sparkling like diamonds in a setting of green.

THREE PIRATES

With spirit   *English*

1. Three pi-rates came to Lon-don town,
2. At first they came to a way-side inn,
3. Oh land-lord, have you good red wine,
4. Oh yes sir, I have good red wine,
5. Oh land-lord, have you hoards of gold,
6. Oh yes sir, I have hoards of gold,
7. Oh land-lord, have you a daugh-ter fair,
8. Oh yes sir, I've a daugh-ter fair,
9. Oh land-lord, will she mar ry me,
10. Oh yes sir, she will mar ry thee,

Yo ho, Yo ho,

Three
At
Oh
Oh
Oh
Oh
Oh
Oh
Oh
Oh

pi-rates came to Lon-don town,
first they came to a way-side inn,
land-lord, have you good red wine,
yes sir, I have good red wine,
land-lord, have you hoards of gold,
yes sir, I have hoards of gold,
land-lord, have you a daugh-ter fair,
yes sir, I've a daugh-ter fair,
land-lord, will she mar ry me,
yes sir, she will mar ry thee,

Yo ho, Yo ho,

Three
At
Oh
Oh
Oh
Oh
Oh
Oh
Oh
Oh

pi - rates came to Lon-don town, To see the king put on his crown,
first they came to a way-side inn, And said "Good land-lord, let us in,"
land-lord, have you good red wine, E-nough to fill this cask of mine?
yes sir, I have good red wine, E-nough to fill this cask of thine?
land-lord, have you hoards of gold, E-nough to fill the af-ter hold?
yes sir, I have hoards of gold, E-nough to fill the af-ter hold,
land-lord, have you a daugh-ter fair, With laugh-ing eyes and cur-ly hair?
yes sir, I've a daugh-ter fair, With laugh-ing eyes and cur-ly hair,
land-lord, will she mar - ry me, And sail with me a-cross the sea?
yes sir, she will mar - ry thee, And sail with thee a-cross the sea,

Yo

ho, you lub-bers, yo ho, you lub-bers, Yo ho! yo ho! yo ho!

Directions for dramatizing the above will be found in "Dramatized Ballads" by Janet E. Tobitt and Alice M. G. White, published by E. P. Dutton and Company, Inc.

THE BROKEN TROTH

Paraphrase by J.E.T.

Czech

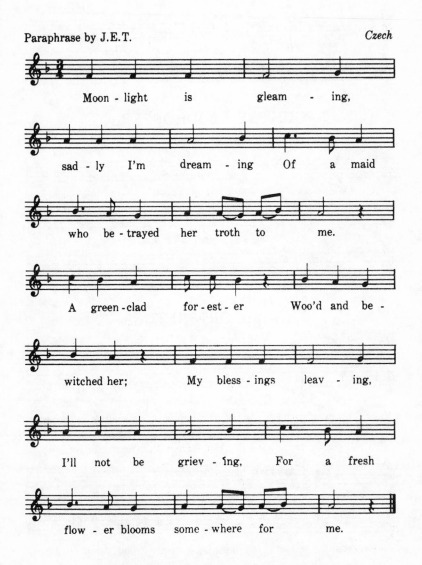

Moon - light is gleam - ing, sad - ly I'm dream - ing Of a maid who be - trayed her troth to me. A green - clad for - est - er Woo'd and be - witched her; My bless - ings leav - ing, I'll not be griev - ing, For a fresh flow - er blooms some - where for me.

JOY IN THE GATES

Six Part Round

16th Century

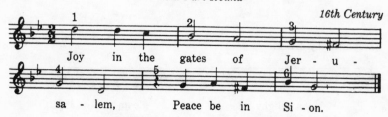

Joy in the gates of Jer - u -
sa - lem, Peace be in Si - on.

COUNTRY CLODHOPPERS

Three Part Round

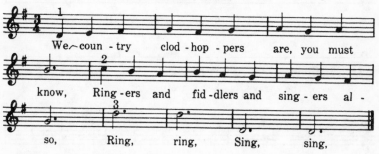

We coun - try clod - hop - pers are, you must
know, Ring - ers and fid - dlers and sing - ers al -
so, Ring, ring, Sing, sing,

THE SAILOR'S RETURN

Translated by
J.E.T.

French

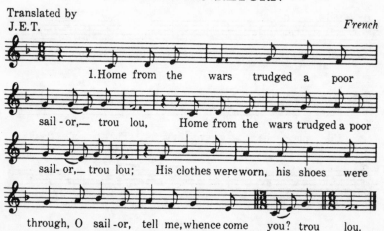

1. Home from the wars trudged a poor
sail - or,— trou lou, Home from the wars trudged a poor
sail - or,— trou lou; His clothes were worn, his shoes were
through, O sail - or, tell me, whence come you? trou lou.

2. Madam, I come straight from sea battles, trou lou,
   Madam, I come straight from sea battles, trou lou,
   Some good white wine of you I pray,
   Then I'll be going on my way, trou lou.

3. Deeply he drank, deeply our sailor, trou lou,
   Deeply he drank, deeply our sailor, trou lou,
   And as he drank began to sing,
   He saw the hostess soft sighing, trou lou.

4. What is amiss, beautiful hostess? trou lou,
   What is amiss, beautiful hostess? trou lou,
   Do you begrudge your wine to me
   Returning homeward from the sea? trou lou.

5. 'Tis not my wine that I regret so, trou lou,
   'Tis not my wine that I regret so, trou lou,
   My husband's dead, therefore my grief,
   You're very like him, past belief, trou lou.

6. Pray tell me true, beautiful hostess, trou lou,
   Pray tell me true, beautiful hostess, trou lou,
   You had by him dear children three,
   Yet now, methinks, a fourth I see, trou lou.

7. Letters they wrote telling false tidings, trou lou,
   Letters they wrote telling false tidings, trou lou,
   "He's dead," they said, "and laid in grave,"
   Myself again in marriage gave, trou lou.

8. Sadly he drank, sadly our sailor, trou lou,
   Sadly he drank, sadly our sailor, trou lou,
   The bitter tears he could not stay,
   He softly went upon his way, trou lou.

This moving old song lends itself readily to dramatic treatment. The **verses** should be expressively sung and drum beats, filling in the musical pauses **after** each of the "trou lou's" played thus ♪♪♪ ♪ ♪ ♪ ♪ | ♩. greatly heighten the effect.

MY LADY GREENSLEEVES

English
16th Century

1. A - las! my love, you do me wrong To cast me off dis - court - eous-ly, And I have lov - ed

CHORUS you so long, De - light - ing in your com - pan-y.

For__ oh, Green-sleeves was all__ my joy, And oh, Green-sleeves was my de-light, And oh, Green-sleeves was my heart of gold, And who but my la - dy Green-sleeves.

2. I bought thee kerchers to thy head
   That were wrought fine and gallantly;
   I kept thee booth at board and bed,
   Which cost my purse well favoredly.

3. Thy smock of silk, both faire and white,
   With gold embroidered gorgeously;
   Thy petticoat of sendal right;
   And these I bought thee gladly.

4. Greensleeves, now, farewell, adieu,
   God I pray to prosper thee!
   For I am still thy lover true,
   Come once again and love me!

This famous old song is found in many variants, it is also a Christmas carol and a dance. Queen Elizabeth was so enraptured by the tune that at one time she ordered part of the church service to be set to it!

THE RISING OF THE LARK

Welsh

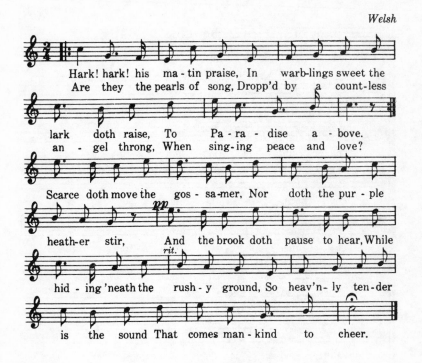

Hark! hark! his ma-tin praise, In warb-lings sweet the
Are they the pearls of song, Dropp'd by a count-less

lark doth raise, To Pa-ra-dise a-bove.
an-gel throng, When sing-ing peace and love?

Scarce doth move the gos-sa-mer, Nor doth the pur-ple

heath-er stir, And the brook doth pause to hear, While

hid-ing 'neath the rush-y ground, So heav'n-ly ten-der

is the sound That comes man-kind to cheer.

Rise, rise, oh lark, then rise
On soft grey wing toward yon skies;
Ascending higher yet:
May no sweet note be lost,
Rise nearer to that happy host,
That earthly pains forget!
Sing and let the wide world hear
Thy melody so sweet and clear,
Waking longing in mankind
To follow to those heights untrod,
Yet nearer day and nearer God,
Eternal Joy to find!

From "The World Sings". By permission of the publishers, The Year Book Press, Ltd., London, England.

QUODLIBET (What you will)

ANON.
Arr. by J. G. H.

The vi - o - lin's ring - ing like love - - ly sing - ing. The

The clar - i - net, the clar - i - net, makes doo - dle, doo - dle, doo - dle, dco - dle det. The

The trump - et is bray - ing, ta - ta - ta - ta - ta - te - ta, ta - ta - ta - ta - ta - te - ta. The

The horn, the horn a - wakes me at morn. The

The drums play - ing two tones and al - ways the same tones. Five,

Divide singers into 5 instrumental parts.

Sing in the following order (a) violin only (b) clarinet only (c) violin and clarinet (d) trumpet only (e) violin, clarinet and trumpet, etc.

By the courtesy of Mr. Julius G. Herford and the Hargail Music Press, New York, N. Y.

A SONG OF THE OPEN AIR

J.E.T.   *Sicilian*

Gaily

1. Come out, the sun is high, the wind is fair;— Come out and join us in the o - pen air. Come out, the sun is high, the wind is fair;— Come out and join us in the o - pen air.

Up hill and down hill, our footsteps rise and fall, Through high - ways and byways, Through for-ests deep and tall. Through for - ests deep and tall, Through for-ests deep and tall; Come out, come out, oh, lis - ten to our call.

A SONG OF THE OPEN AIR

(continued)

2. Come out, the moon is high, the wind is fair;
Come out and join us in the open air.
Come out, the moon is high, the wind is fair;
Come out and join us in the open air.
High notes, and low notes, our voices rise and fall
In glad songs and sad songs, in round and madrigal,
In round and madrigal, in round and madrigal;
Come out, come out, oh, listen to our call.

THE WIND MILL

Three Part Round

TWO DUCKS ON A POND

Three Part Round

Two ducks on a pond, Wib-ble, wob-ble, wib-ble, wob-ble, Two ducks on a pond, Wib-ble, wob-ble, wib-ble, wob-ble, Two old la-dies go-ing to mar-ket, Wib-bi-ly wib-bi-ly wob-ble, wib-bi-ly wib-bi-ly wob-ble.

GOOD NIGHT TO YOU ALL

Three Part Round

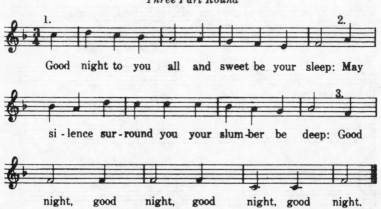

Good night to you all and sweet be your sleep: May si-lence sur-round you your slum-ber be deep: Good night, good night, good night, good night.

J.E.T.   *Mexican*

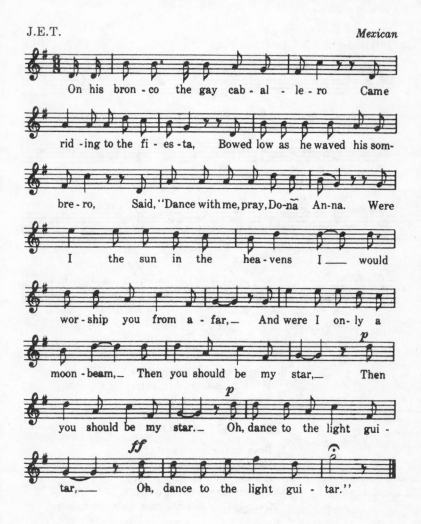

On his bron-co the gay cab-al-le-ro Came rid-ing to the fi-es-ta, Bowed low as he waved his som-bre-ro, Said, "Dance with me, pray, Do-ña An-na. Were I the sun in the hea-vens I —— would wor-ship you from a-far, —— And were I on-ly a moon-beam, —— Then you should be my star, —— Then you should be my star. —— Oh, dance to the light gui-tar, —— Oh, dance to the light gui-tar."

In Mexico it is customary for a gentleman to ask a lady to dance with a flowery poem or song.

NICE GIRLS DON'T CHASE THE BOYS

Translated by J.E.T.   *French*

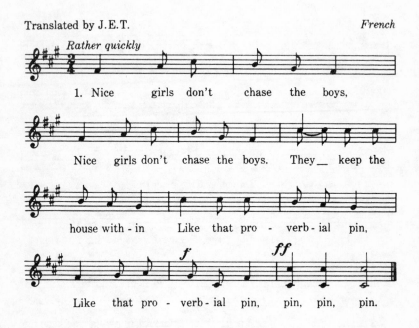

1. Nice girls don't chase the boys,
   Nice girls don't chase the boys.
   They — keep the house with-in
   Like that pro-verb-ial pin,
   Like that pro-verb-ial pin, pin, pin, pin.

2. When houses brightly shine,
   When houses brightly shine,
   Young men call in a row
   Call — but forget to go,
   Call — but forget to go, go, go, go.

3. Boys on the hope-chest sit,
   Boys on the hope-chest sit,
   If kicks show an empty store,
   Quickly they seek the door,
   Quickly they seek the door, door, door, door.

COCKLES AND MUSSELS

English

1. In Dub-lin's fair ci-ty, where girls are so pret-ty, I first set my eyes on sweet Mol-lie Ma-lone As she pushed her wheel-bar-row Through streets broad and nar-row Cry-ing coc-kles and mus-sels a - live, a - live, oh!

CHORUS *f* (*last time pp*)

A - live, a-live, oh! A - live, a-live, oh! Cry-ing coc-kles and mus-sels a - live, a - live, oh!

2. She was a fishmonger, but sure 'twas no wonder,
   For so were her father and mother before,
   And they each pushed their wheel-barrow
   Through streets broad and narrow
   Crying cockles and mussels alive, alive, oh!

3. She died of a "faver", and no one could save her,
   And that was the end of sweet Mollie Malone;
   Her ghost wheels her barrow
   Through streets broad and narrow
   Crying cockles and mussels alive, alive, oh!

NOW COMES THE HOUR

LUDWIG VAN BEETHOVEN
(1770-1827)

Quietly and slowly

Now comes the hour for peace - ful

Ah

Now comes the hour for peace - ful

rest,   Oh, how   blest!   peace - ful   rest.

peace - ful   rest.

rest,   Oh, how   blest!   peace - ful   rest.

The above may be used as a vesper part-song or as a three part round. In either case the second line should be subdued to the role of a hummed accompaniment.

PEACE OF THE RIVER

(Written on the Kentucky River)

GLENDORA GOSLING   VIOLA WOOD

Slowly, with expression

Peace I ask of thee, O Riv-er, Peace, peace, peace.

When I learn to live se-rene-ly Cares will cease.

From the hills I gath-er cour-age, Vi-sion of the day to be;

Strength to lead, and faith to fol-low, All are giv-en un-to me.

Peace I ask of thee, O Riv-er, Peace, peace, peace.

Used by permission

WHY SHOULDN'T MY GOOSE?

Four Part Round

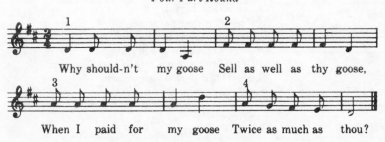

Why should-n't my goose Sell as well as thy goose,

When I paid for my goose Twice as much as thou?

O WERT THOU IN THE CAULD BLAST

Robert Burns

FELIX MENDELSSOHN
(1809-1847)

Andante

1. O wert thou in the cauld blast On yon-der lea, on
yon-der lea, My plaid-ie to the an-gry airt, I'd
shel-ter thee, I'd shel-ter thee! Or did mis-for-tune's
bit-ter storms A-round thee blaw, a-round thee blaw,
Thy bield should be my bo-som To
share it a', to share it a'.

2. Or were I in the wildest waste,
   Sae black and bare, sae black and bare,
   The desert were a paradise
   If thou wert there, if thou wert there.
   Or were I monarch of the globe
   With thee to reign, with thee to reign,
   The brightest jewel in my crown
   Wad be my queen, wad be my queen.

bield — shelter

COSSACK'S LULLABY

Translation anonymous   *Nicholas Bachmetieff (1807-1891)*

1. Sleep, ah, sleep, my dar - ling ba - by, Su, su, lul - la - by;____ See, the moon is watch - ing o'er thee, Peace - ful - ly on high.____ Thou shalt hear a won - drous sto - ry, Close each wake - ful eye: ____ And a song as well I'll sing thee, Su, su, lul - la - by. ____

2. All too soon wilt thou be learning
   Of a warrior's life;
   With the gun and prancing war-horse
   Moving to the strife.
   Saddle, bridle, all my baby
   Shall have by and bye;
   Now, my darling, thou must slumber,
   Su, su, lullaby.

O HUSH THEE, MY BABIE

WALTER SCOTT

ARTHUR SULLIVAN (1842-1900)
Descant by H.A. Chambers

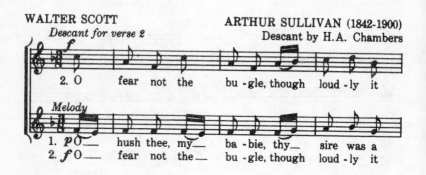

Descant for verse 2

2. O fear not the bu-gle, though loud-ly it

Melody

1. *p* O hush thee, my babie, thy sire was a
2. *f* O fear not the bu-gle, though loud-ly it

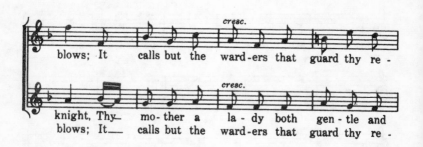

blows; It calls but the ward-ers that guard thy re-

knight, Thy mo-ther a la-dy both gen-tle and
blows; It calls but the ward-ers that guard thy re-

pose, guard thy re-pose. Their

bright, both gen-tle and bright; *p* The woods and the
pose, that guard thy re-pose. *mf* Their bows would be

O HUSH THEE, MY BABIE

(continued)

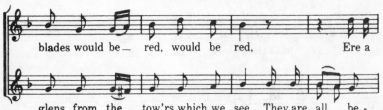

blades would be — red, would be red, Ere a

glens from the — tow'rs which we see, They are all — be -
bend - ed, their — blades would be red, Ere the step of a

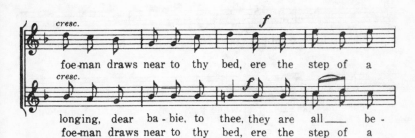

foe - man draws near to thy bed, ere the step of a

longing, dear ba - bie, to thee, they are all —— be -
foe - man draws near to thy bed, ere the step of a

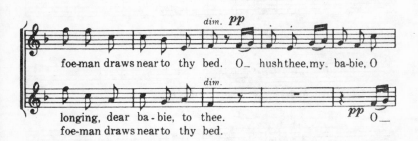

foe - man draws near to thy bed. O — hush thee, my — ba - bie, O

longing, dear ba - bie, to thee.
foe - man draws near to thy bed.
O —

hush ————— thee, O — hush thee, my ba - - bie.

hush thee, O — hush thee, my ba - - - bie.

O HUSH THEE, MY BABIE

(continued)

3. O— hush thee, my— ba-bie, the— time will soon come, When thy sleep will be bro-ken by trum-pet and drum, by trum-pet and drum. Then— hush thee, my— dar-ling, take— rest while you may, For strife comes with man-hood, and wa-king with day, for strife comes with man-hood, and wa - king with day. O— hush thee, my— ba-bie, O hush — thee, O hush— thee, O hush thee, O hush thee, my ba - bie. ———

PEASANT CHORUS

from

"Faust"

CHARLES GOUNOD (1818-1893)

Ah! _____

Rise, O sleep-y maid-en, Where-fore dreaming still?_

Ro-sy morn is break-ing, Sun-beams drench the hill;_

Blithe birds are sing-ing, Oh, lis-ten to their song,_

Gold - en corn ____ is ri - pen-ing, The

har - vest won't be long. Streams and spark-ling

brook-lets Op-en smil-ing eyes,_ To

Joy all Na-ture a - wak-ens, O maid-en, a-

rise!_ To Joy all Na-ture a-wak-ens, O maid-en, rise.

Translated by J.E.T.

J.S. BACH (1685-1750)
melody J: CRÜGER (1648)

1. O God, Who art the on - ly light, Whose Truth lives ev - er
Thy pow'r hath chased dark night a - way, And bright-ly dawns a-

in our sight, To Thee be praise and sing - ing!
oth - er day, Thy glor-ious work re - veal - ing.

Thy mer-cy held us in our sleep Its nev-er fail-ing watch did keep.

2. Our hearts alone belong to Thee,
   O grant that we may worthy be
   When earthly life is ending.
   And when Thy summons strikes our ear
   May we with joyful steps appear,
   Thy heavenly court attending.
   Stretch out Thy hand so full of grace
   That we may see Thee face to face.

WHEN YOUR POTATO'S DONE
(*Quan' Patate La Cuite*)

J.E.T.

U.S. Creole

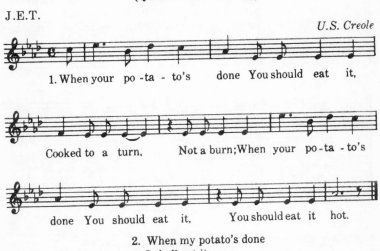

1. When your po-ta-to's done You should eat it,
Cooked to a turn, Not a burn; When your po-ta-to's
done You should eat it, You should eat it hot.

2. When my potato's done
   I shall eat it,
   Frizzled or charred,
   Soft or hard;
   When my potato's done
   I shall eat it,
   If it's good or not!

The above is the tune of a Bamboula, a dance of African rhythm which used to be danced on the Place Congo in New Orleans; the constant repetition of one note suggests the drum beat.

Sometimes the song is used to announce to children that a meal is ready.

THE SPACIOUS FIRMAMENT ON HIGH
(*Creation*)

JOSEPH ADDISON

FRANZ JOSEF HAYDN
(1732-1809)

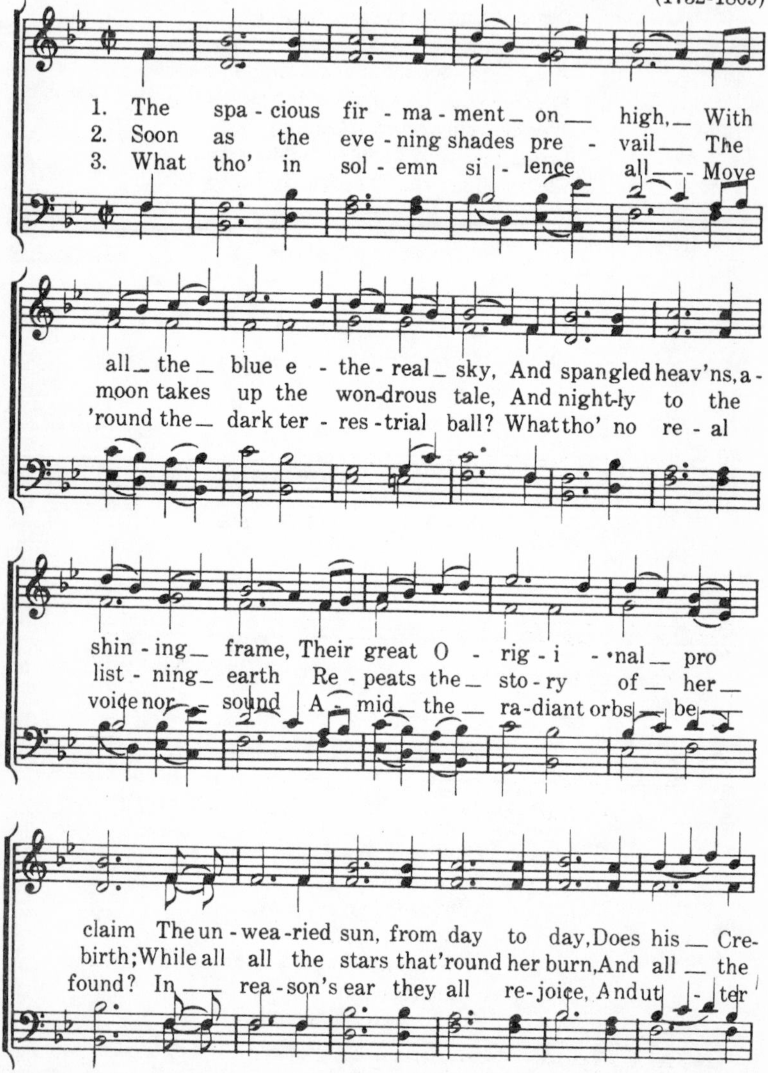

1. The spa-cious fir-ma-ment on high, With all the blue e-the-real sky, And spangled heav'ns, a shin-ing frame, Their great O-rig-i-nal pro claim The un-wea-ried sun, from day to day, Does his Cre-

2. Soon as the eve-ning shades pre-vail The moon takes up the won-drous tale, And night-ly to the list-ning earth Re-peats the sto-ry of her birth; While all all the stars that'round her burn, And all the

3. What tho' in sol-emn si-lence all Move 'round the dark ter-res-trial ball? What tho' no re-al voice nor sound Amid the ra-diant orbs be found? In rea-son's ear they all re-joice, And ut-ter

a - tor's pow'rs dis-play, And pub - lish-es to
plan - ets in_ their turn, Con-firm the ti - dings
forth a glo - riousvoice, For- ev - er sing - ing

ev - 'ry land The work_ of an_ Al-might-y Hand.
as they roll, And spread the truth from pole to pole.
as they shine, "The Hand that made us is Di - vine."

By permission. From "Songs We Sing", published by Hall and McCreary
Company, Chicago

OH, DEAR, WHAT CAN THE MATTER BE?

English–16th Century
Arranged by J.E.T.

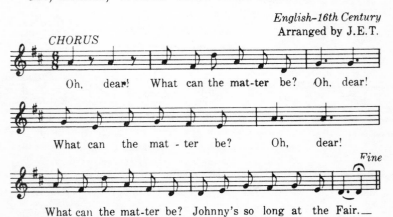

CHORUS

Oh, dear! What can the mat-ter be? Oh, dear!

What can the mat - ter be? Oh, dear!

Fine

What can the mat-ter be? Johnny's so long at the Fair._

OH, DEAR, WHAT CAN THE MATTER BE?

(continued)

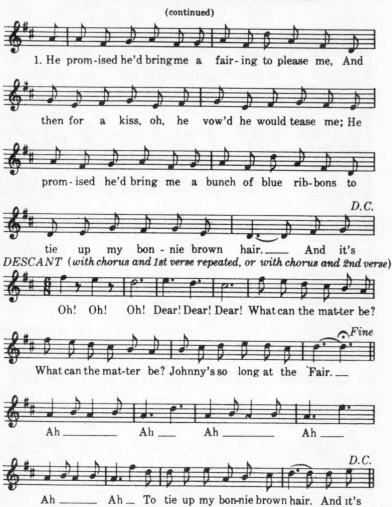

1. He prom-ised he'd bring me a fair-ing to please me, And

then for a kiss, oh, he vow'd he would tease me; He

prom-ised he'd bring me a bunch of blue rib-bons to

D.C.

tie up my bon-nie brown hair.___ And it's

DESCANT (with chorus and 1st verse repeated, or with chorus and 2nd verse)

Oh! Oh! Oh! Dear! Dear! Dear! What can the mat-ter be?

Fine

What can the mat-ter be? Johnny's so long at the 'Fair.___

Ah_____ Ah__ Ah_____ Ah___

D.C.

Ah_____ Ah__ To tie up my bon-nie brown hair. And it's

2. He promised he'd bring me a basket of posies,
   A garland of lilies, a garland of roses;
   A little straw hat to set off the blue ribbons,
   That tie up my bonnie brown hair.

English version by J.E.T.

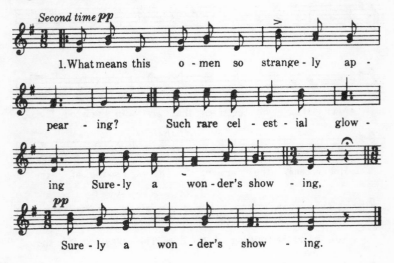

Second time **pp**

1. What means this o - men so strange - ly ap - pear - ing? Such rare cel - est - ial glow - ing Sure - ly a won - der's show - ing,

pp

Sure - ly a won - der's show - ing.

2. Born is the ruler of earth and of Heaven,
   Born is the ruler of earth ánd of Heaven;
   Christ in a manger's lying,
   All are to Bethlehem hieing,
   All are to Bethlehem hieing.

3. Thanks for existence on His holy birthday,
   Thanks for existence on His holy birthday;
   Let us give adoration,
   He's come for our salvation,
   He's come for our salvation.

THE HOLLY AND THE IVY

arranged by J.E.T.

Traditional

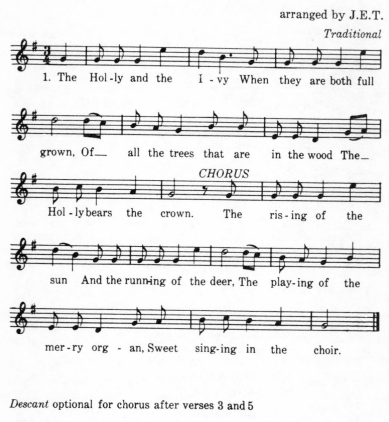

1. The Hol-ly and the I-vy When they are both full grown, Of__ all the trees that are in the wood The__ Hol-ly bears the crown.

CHORUS

The ris-ing of the sun And the runn-ing of the deer, The play-ing of the mer-ry org - an, Sweet sing-ing in the choir.

Descant optional for chorus after verses 3 and 5

The ris-ing of the sun The running of the deer, The

play-ing of the mer-ry org-an, Sweet sing-ing in the choir.

(continued)

2. The Holly bears a blossom
   As white as the lily flower,
   And Mary bore sweet Jesus Christ
   To be our sweet Savior.

3. The Holly bears a berry
   As red as any blood,
   And Mary bore sweet Jesus Christ
   To do poor sinners good.

4. The Holly bears a prickle
   As sharp as any thorn,
   And Mary bore sweet Jesus Christ
   On Christmas Day in the morn.

5. The Holly bears a bark
   As bitter as any gall,
   And Mary bore sweet Jesus Christ
   For to redeem us all.

SANTY ANNA

U.S. Capstan Shanty

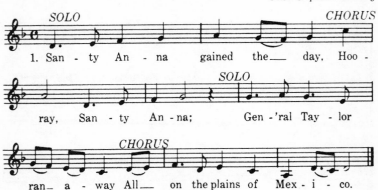

1. Santy Anna gained the day, Hooray, Santy Anna; Gen-'ral Taylor ran away All on the plains of Mexico.

2. Santy Anna fought for fame,
   That's where Santy gained his name.

3. Santy Anna's day is o'er,
   Santy Anna will fight no more.

This shanty dates from shortly after the war between the U. S. and Mexico. For some unknown reason the sailors in their song made Santy Anna the victor, whereas he was actually beaten and fled into exile.

PRAISE TO GOD, IMMORTAL PRAISE

H. MAITLAND BARNES

1. Praise to God, im-mortal praise, For the love that crowns our days;

Bounteous Source of ev-'ry joy, Let Thy praise our songs em-ploy:

For the blessings of the field, For the stores the gardens yield,

For the wine's exalted juice, For the gen'rous olive's use,

(Continued)

2. Flocks that whiten all the plain,
   Yellow leaves of ripened grain,
   Clouds that drop their fattening dews,
   Suns that temperate warmth diffuse;
   All that Spring with bounteous hand
   Scatters o'er the smiling land,
   All that liberal Autumn pours
   From her rich o'erflowing stores.

3. Should the vine put forth no more,
   Nor the olive yield her store;
   Though the sickening flocks should fall,
   And the herds desert the stall,
   Yet to Thee our souls shall raise
   Grateful vows and solemn praise,
   And when every blessing's flown
   Love Thee for Thyself alone.

                    Barbauld

By kind permission of Mrs. H. Maitland Barnes.

NAVAJO HAPPY SONG

Recorded by Marguerite Twohy in New Mexico. The words mean no more than "tr la la" and the song is sung at feasts and on other joyous occasions. Sing it through three times, adding the last two measures for the finale; the last "yah" is shouted.

CANTICLE

1st group   Russian

1. For the sun in heav'n that wak - ens and warms with its bright - ness, glo - ri - a.

2nd group

For the moon and stars that chase the dark and cheer with their light - ness, glo - ri - a.

CANTICLE

(Continued)

1st group
2. For the trees and flowers, for fruits and the harvest's rich treasure,
gloria.

2nd group
For the birds and beasts, for sights and sounds that fill us with
pleasure, gloria.

1st group
3. For good health and strength, for wit, and for mental endeavor,
gloria.

2nd group
For our home and friends, for laughter and song praise forever,

Both groups
GLORIA!

The above tune was used by Moussorgsky in the Coronation Scene of "Boris
Godounov"; Beethoven also used it in one of his quartets.

THE EVENING STAR

HOFFMANN VON FALLERSLEBEN
Translated by J.E.T.

ROBERT SCHUMANN
(1810-1856)

1. O glo-ri-ous star, How kind-ly you are; A-bove in the hea-vens You shine from a-far.

2. O eye gleaming bright,
   Celestial light!
   My heart's full of gladness
   Although it be night.

3. I gaze from below,
   Your heavenly glow
   Will guard me and guide me
   Wherever I go.

WHO IS THE MAN?

U.S. Pilgrim Hymn
Arranged by ELIE SIEGMEISTER

1. Who is the man that life doth will; That lov-eth dayes, good for to see? Re-freyn-ing, keep thy tongue from yll, Thy lips from speak-ing fal-la-cee. Do good, and e-vil quite es-chew, Seek peace and af-ter it pur-sew.

2. In all times bless the Lord will I,
   His praise within my mouth, alway.
   My soul shall in the Lord glory;
   The meek shall heare, and joy shall they.
   O magnifie the Lord with me,
   His name together extoll we.

3. I saw Jah and he me answered;
   And from my fears all, rid me free.
   To him they looked and flowed;
   And ashamed let not their faces bee.
   Jah heard when this poor man did call:
   And saved him from his troubles all.

4. Jehovah's angel camp doth lay
   'Bout them that fear him; and frees them.
   Taste ye and see that good is Jah:
   O blest man, that hopes in him.
   Fear ye Jehovah, saints of his:
   For to his fearers, want none is.

5. Evil shall cause the wicked die:
   And haters of the just man, they
   Shall be condemned as guilty.
   His servants' soul, redeem doth Jah:
   And they shall not be judged unjust,
   All that in him for safety trust.

Jah — Jehovah

This lovely old hymn was in the Ainsworth Psalter, the only printed music book brought to America by the Pilgrims.

From "A Treasury of American Song" by Olin Downes and Elie Siegmeister, published by Howell, Soskin and Company, New York. Music copyright, 1940, by Elie Siegmeister.

WASSAIL SONG

Traditional

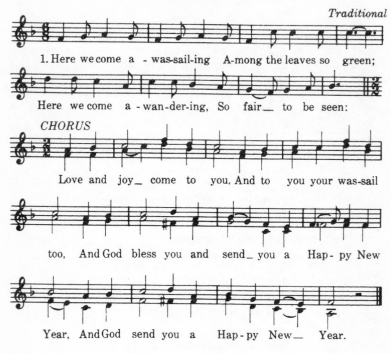

1. Here we come a - was-sail-ing A-mong the leaves so green;
Here we come a - wan-der-ing, So fair— to be seen:

CHORUS

Love and joy— come to you, And to you your was-sail
too, And God bless you and send— you a Hap-py New
Year, And God send you a Hap-py New— Year.

2. We are not daily beggars
   That beg from door to door,
   But we are neighbors' children
   Whom you have seen before.

3. We have got a little purse
   Of ratching leather skin;
   We want some of your small change
   To line it well within.

4. God bless the Master of this house,
   Likewise the Mistress too,
   And all the little children
   That round the table go.

Wassail — an Anglo-Saxon word meaning "be whole", a toast.

Ratching — interlaced

MAGNIFICAT

Hebrew

Air: Az Yashir

Words from Psalm CL

Ha - le - lu - jah, Ha - le - lu - jah!

Praise ye the Lord in his sanc - tua - ry and

fir - ma - ment of pow'r, Give praise for might - y acts and

exc - 'llent great - ness, Praise ye the Lord. With

harp and dance and cym - bals, With psal - try give

praise, And with or - gan and strings and tim - brels Your

trum - pets loud - ly raise, Let ev'-ry - thing on earth that

breath - ing is un - to the Lord give— praise.

YOURS FOR A SONG

MARGOT, DRESS THE VINES

English version by
   J. E. T.

from the French
16th century

Mar-got, dress the vines, I pray you, gai - ly,
gai - ly, dress the vines. Mar-got, dress the vines, I
pray you, gai - ly. In Lor - raine when I was
walk-ing, Mar - got, In Lor-raine when I was walk-ing, Mar -
got, There I heard three cap-tains talk - ing, Mar -
got, There I heard three cap-tains talk-ing, Mar - got.

They said I was very ugly, Margot,
I am not so very ugly, Margot.

I am not so very ugly, Margot,
Since the King's own son he loves me, Margot.

He a sign of troth declaring, Margot,
Gave me marj'ram sweet, scent-bearing, Margot.

If it thrives as queen I'll reign, O Margot!
If it dies I'll lose my pain, O Margot!

EL QUELÉLE
(The White Hawk)

English version by
CHARLES E. LUMMIS

Spanish Californian

Pa - pa Que - lé - le has died, ay, ay, ay, ay, ay!

Died as the morn - ing was break - - ing;

Pa - pa Que - lé - le has died, ay, ay, ay, ay, ay!

Now to his grave he must go.___ Three dra -

goons and a corp - 'ral, Ay, ay, ay, ay, ay, ay!

Tom-cat for sac - ris - tan too.___ And all the

ba - by Que - lé - les, Ay, ay, ay, ay, ay,

ay! Cry them to death in their woe.___

From "Spanish Songs of Old California," Chas. F. Lummis and Arthur Farwell.
Copyright owner and publisher G. Schirmer, Inc., New York City, N.Y. By permission.

THE DEAF WOMAN'S COURTSHIP

United States-Appalachian

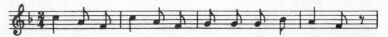

Old wo-man, old wo-man, are you fond of smok-ing?

Old wo-man, old wo-man, are you fond of smok-ing?

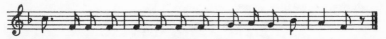

Speak a lit-tle loud-er, sir, I'm rath-er hard of hear-ing.

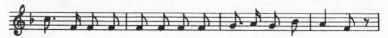

Speak a lit-tle loud-er, sir, I'm rath-er hard of hear-ing.

Old woman, old woman, are you fond of carding?
Old woman, old woman, are you fond of carding?
Speak a little louder, sir, I'm rather hard of hearing.
Speak a little louder, sir, I'm rather hard of hearing.

Old woman, old woman, will you let me court you?
Old woman, old woman, will you let me court you?
Speak a little louder, sir, I just begin to hear you.
Speak a little louder, sir, I just begin to hear you.

Old woman, old woman, don't you want to marry me?
Old woman, old woman, don't you want to marry me?
Lord have mercy on my soul, I think that now I hear you!
Lord have mercy on my soul, I think that now I hear you!

THE APPLE-CHEEKED RIDER

English version by
FJERIL HESS

Slovak

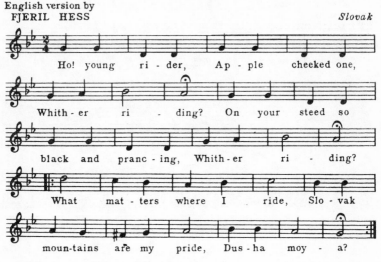

Ho! young ri - der, Ap - ple cheeked one,

Whith - er ri - ding? On your steed so

black and pranc - ing, Whith - er ri - ding?

What mat - ters where I ride, Slo - vak

moun-tains are my pride, Dus - ha moy - a?

Dusha moya — little sweetheart.

DE BEZEM
(The Broom)
Four part round

Dutch

De be - zem, de be - zem, Wat doe je er mee? Wat

doe je er mee? Wij ve - gen er mee, Wij

ve - gen er mee, De vloer aan, de vloer ann!

This amusing round from Holland is already somewhat known in the U.S. Literally it **means** — "The broom, the broom, what do you do with it? We sweep up the floor, the floor!"

Phonetically	*bezem* — bayzum	*doe* — doo
	je — ya	*er* — air
	mee — may	*wij* — way
	vegen — faygan	*vloer* — fluur

FISHERMEN'S EVENING SONG

K. T. SIZER

Breton Air

One song my com-rades, ere we go, (Lis-ten to the glad waves' call!) The tide runs high, the sun sinks low, (Lis-ten to the wild waves' call!) We toil while oth-ers sleep, ("Hark! they call, wild waves' call!) Far sail-ing o'er the deep. (Lis-ten to the deep waves' call!)

One cheer, my comrades, ere we go,
A Breton fisher fears no foe;
'Mid rocks and whirlpool's dread
Boldly we seek our bread.

One look, my comrades, ere we go,
Our seaport town lies safe and low,
Sleep soft, dear friends at home,
Sleep. while we cross the foam.

One pray'r, my comrades, ere we go,
For waves may roar and tempests blow,
Lord, let Thy strong arm be
'Round all who toil at sea!

By permission, from Curwen Edition No. 6268, published by J. Curwen and Sons, Ltd., 24 Berners Street, London, W. 1. England.

GO TO SLEEPY

United States- Georgia

Go to sleep-y, lit-tle ba-by,

'Fo' de boo-ger man ketch you. When you wake you'll

have a piece of cake And a whole lot of lit-tle hors-es.

Go to sleep-y, lit-tle ba-by, 'Fo' de boo-ger man

ketch you. When you wake you shall have a cake,

coach and four lit-tle po-nies. A black and a bay, and a

dap-ple and a gray. Go to sleep-y, lit-tle ba-by.

GRÜN, GRÜN, GRÜN

German

Grün, grün, grün, sind al - le mei - ne Klei - der,

Grün, grün, grün liebt je - der - man. Dar - um lieb' ich

al - les was so grün ist, Denn mein Lieb ein Jä - ger ist.

Blau, blau, blau sind alle meine Kleider,
Blau, blau, blau liebt jederman.
Darum lieb' ich alles was so blau ist,
Denn mein Lieb ein Matrose ist.

Weiss, weiss, weiss sind alle meine Kleider,
Weiss, weiss, weiss liebt jederman.
Darum lieb' ich alles was so weiss ist,
Denn mein Lieb ein Bäcker ist.

Schwarz, schwarz, schwarz sind alle meine Kleider,
Schwarz, schwarz, schwarz liebt jederman.
Darum lieb' ich alles was so schwarz ist,
Denn mein Lieb ein Schornsteinfeger ist.

The language of this song is so simple that most people enjoy singing it in the
original tongue. Translated literally the first verse is:

Green, green, green are all of my dresses, green, green, green loves everyone.
So I love everything that's green because my love is a hunter.

Blau - blue   *Matrose* - sailor   *Weiss* - white   *Bäcker* - baker

Schwarz - black   *Schornsteinfeger* - chimneysweep

GYPSY SONG

English version by
V. M. S.

German - Swiss

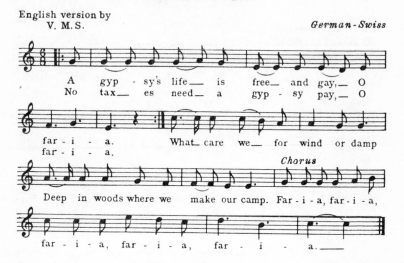

A gyp - sy's life— is free— and gay,— O far - i - a.
No tax— es need— a gyp - sy pay,— O far - i - a.

What— care we— for wind or damp Deep in woods where we make our camp.

Chorus

Far - i - a, far - i - a, far - i - a, far - i - a, far - i - a.—

And should hunger us assail,
Quickly then we're on the trail.
"Little deer, look out, look out,
When the gypsy's gun speaks out."

Thirst it is a cruel thing,
But we know a clear, cool spring,
Where the water tastes like wine,
Bubbling out like champagne fine.

Feather beds we do not sleep on,
But a hole we dig and deepen,
Moss and twigs we then pile in,
What better' bed can a man sleep in?

When the sun has sunk down low
In a circle camp fires glow
Nut-brown maiden, dance therein,
While I scrape on the old violin.

Faria - pronounce fair-ee-a

From "Pfadfinderinnenlieder" by permission of the Swiss Girl Guides Federation and from "The World Sings" by permission of The Year Book Press, Ltd., London, England.

AT SUMMER MORN

Three part round

At summer morn the mer-ry lark her - alds in the day;

At e-ven-tide sad Phil-o - mel breathes her plaintive lay,

Warb-ling sweet - ly all her grief a-way.

HUSH-A-BA, BIRDIE

Scottish

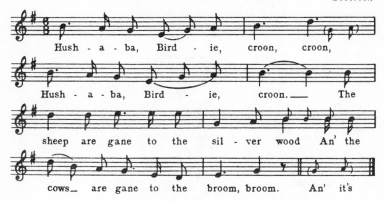

Hush - a - ba, Bird - ie, croon, croon,

Hush - a - ba, Bird - ie, croon.___ The

sheep are gane to the sil - ver wood An' the

cows___ are gane to the broom, broom. An' it's

An' it's braw, braw milking the kye, kye,
An' it's braw milking the kye,
The birds are singing, the bells are ringing,
The wild deer come galloping by, by.

Hush-a-ba, Birdie, croon, croon,
Hush-a-ba, Birdie, croon,
The gaits are gane to the mountains hie,
An' they'll no' be hame till noon, noon.

Braw-fine, kye-cows, gaits-goats.

I WONDER WHEN I SHALL BE MARRIED

United States

I won-der when I shall be mar-ried, Be
mar-ried, be mar-ried, I won-der when I shall be
mar-ried, For my beau-ty's be-gin-ning to fade.

My father has forty good shillings,
Good shillings, good shillings,
My father has forty good shillings,
And they'll be all mine when he dies.

My mother is ready and willing,
And willing, and willing,
My mother is ready and willing,
For she has four daughters besides.

My shoes have gone to be mended,
Be mended, be mended,
My shoes have gone to be mended,
And my petticoat gone to dye green.

They're going to be ready by Sunday,
By Sunday, by Sunday,
They're going to be ready by Sunday,
Oh, say, won't I look like a queen?

A spoon and a cup and a trencher,
A trencher, a trencher,
A spoon and a cup and a trencher,
And a candlestick made out of clay.

Oh, say, won't I be a bargain,
A bargain, a bargain,
Oh, say, won't I be a bargain,
For someone to carry away?

From Handy 11 manual, transcribed by Miss Lulu M. Hale, Ary. Kentucky. By permission of the publishers, the Cooperative Recreation Service, Delaware, Ohio.

LET US GO A-MAYING

Three part round

JOHN HILTON (1599-1659)

1. Come let us all a-May-ing go, And
2. The bells shall ring, the bells shall ring, and the
3. drums shall beat, the fife shall play, and

1. light-ly and light-ly trip it to and fro;
2. cuck-oo, the cuck-oo, the cuck-oo sing; The
3. so we'll pass our time a-way.

LULLABY

Zulu

Lu-la, ba-by, la, la, Whem shell quam, K'
sa-sa am ka-bel-la, Whem shell quam.

This song readily lends itself to spontaneous harmony.

LIGHTSOME HEART
(Froh zu sein)

English version by
J. E. T.

Four part round

AUGUST MÜHLING (1786-1847)

Light - some heart gives tru - est pleas - ure,

Wealth be - yond a king - ly treas - ure.

LAVENDER'S BLUE

Old English

Lav - en - der's blue, dil - ly dil - ly, Lav - en - der's green,

When I'm a King, dil - ly, dil - ly, You shall be Queen.

Who told you so, dil - ly, dil - ly, Who told you so?

'Twas my own heart, dil - ly, dil - ly, That told me so.

Call up your men, dilly, dilly,
Set them to work,
Some with a rake, dilly, dilly,
Some with a fork,
Some to make hay, dilly, dilly,
Some to thresh corn,
While you and I, dilly, dilly,
Keep ourselves warm.

If it should hap, dilly, dilly,
If it should chance,
We shall be gay, dilly, dilly,
We shall both dance.
Lavender's blue, dilly, dilly,
Lavender's green,
When I'm a King, dilly, dilly,
You shall be Queen.

MY BONNY CUCKOO

Ireland

My bon - ny cuck - oo— I tell you true, That thro' the groves, I'll rove with you; I'll rove with you un-til the next spring, And then my cuck-oo— shall sweet-ly sing.

> The ash and the hazel shall mourning say,
> My bonny cuckoo, don't go away,
> Don't go away, but tarry here,
> And make the season last all the year.

From "The World Sings." By permission of the publishers, The Year Book Press, Ltd., London, England.

JOG ON, JOG ON

SHAKESPEARE   *Traditional Sixteenth Century*

Jog on, jog on, the foot - path way,— And mer - ri - ly hent the stile - a! A mer - ry heart goes all— the day, Your sad— tires in a mile - a.

hent - catch hold of

This is sung in "The Winter's Tale" by that merry rogue, Autolycus. When sung quickly and repeated without any pauses it makes an excellent hiking song.

MY LOVYER IS A SAILOR BOY

United States - New England

My lov - yer is a sail - or boy so—
gal - yant and— bold; He's— tall as a—
flag— staff on - ly nine - teen years—
old, And he sails o'er the— wide seas to—
lands far— and near, And my heart it is a -
heav - i - ing be - cause he is not here.

His parents had bonded him for to be a carpenteer,
But a sea-faring life he did very much prefeer;
His spirits was so tormentuous and so fierce to behold,
This young man bred a carpenteer, only nineteen years old.

My heart it is a-heav-i-ing just like the rolling sea
For fear his affect-shi-uns don't still p'int towards me;
For there's young gals in all parts of the world I am told,
Especially for a young man only nineteen years old.

Recorded from the singing of Miss Clara Rawson, Providence, R.I. 1933 by Miss Marie Gaudette. Used by permission.

THE PLOUGHBOY

Three part round

W. W. PEARSON

From "Graduated Rounds." By permission of the publishers, Novello and Company, London, England. United States agent, The H.W. Gray Company, New York, N.Y.

ROBIN HOOD AND LITTLE JOHN

Cornish May Dance

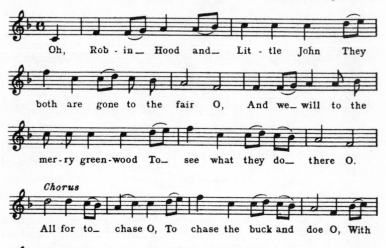

Oh, Rob-in— Hood and— Lit-tle John They
both are gone to the fair O, And we— will to the
mer-ry green-wood To— see what they do— there O.

Chorus

All for to— chase O, To chase the buck and doe O, With
hal-an-tow, jol-ly rum-ble O, To chase the buck and doe O.

As for those gay Spaniards
Who make so great a boast, O,
They shall eat grey goose feathers
And we shall eat the roast, O.

And we were up as soon as day
For to fetch the summer home, O,
The summer and the May
Now winter is agone, O.

The Cornish dance belonging to the above tune makes a delightful introduction to a May festival. The dancers move forward to the first eight measures, in couples, taking three running steps and a hop in each measure. During the first four measures of the chorus each set of two couples takes right hands across, with the same steps, proceeding in clockwise direction; during the last four measures left hands across, dancing in counter-clockwise direction. With the exception of the "sets of four" circles the dance is a processional and by means of it the group may be led to any required position.

Hal-an-tow sometimes thought to mean heel and toe. More probably an old name for the garlanding round the maypole.

THE SONG OF THE SHIP-BUILDERS

(Two part canon)

JOHN GREENLEAF WHITTIER   GUSTAV HOLST (1874 - 1934)

Hark! roars the bel lows, blast on blast, The

soot - y smith - y— jars, And fire - sparks ris - ing

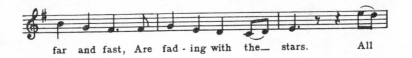

far and fast, Are fad - ing with the— stars. All

day for us the smith shall stand, Be - side that flash-ing

forge; All day for us his heav - y hand, The

groan-ing an - vil scourge. From far off hills the

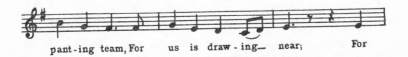

pant-ing team, For us is draw - ing— near; For

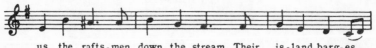

us the rafts-men down the stream, Their is-land barg-es_

steer.   Rings out for us the axe-man's stroke In

for - ests old and still, For us the cen-tu-ry

cir - cled oak, Falls crash - ing down his hill.

Where'er the keel of our good ship
    The sea's rough field shall plough,
Where'er her tossing spars shall drip
    With saltspray caught below,
That ship must heed her master's beck,
    Her helm obey his hand,
And seamen tread her reeling deck
    As if they trod the land.
Be hers the Prairie's golden grain,
    The Desert's golden sand,
The clustered fruits of sunny Spain,
    The spice of Morningland!
Her pathway on the open main
    May blessings follow free,
And glad hearts welcome back again
    Her white sails from the sea!

SPIN, SPIN

English version by
J. E. T.

German

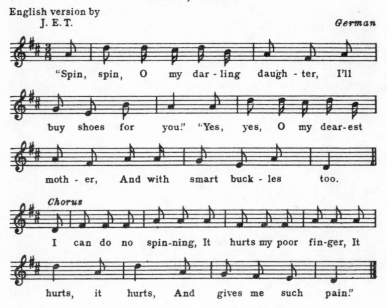

"Spin, spin, O my dar - ling daugh - ter, I'll buy shoes for you." "Yes, yes, O my dear-est moth - er, And with smart buck - les too.

Chorus

I can do no spin-ning, It hurts my poor fin-ger, It hurts, it hurts, And gives me such pain."

"Spin, spin, O my darling daughter,
I'll buy stockings thin."
"Yes, yes, O my dearest mother.
And with gay clocks therein."

"Spin, spin, O my darling daughter,
I'll buy a dress fine."
"Yes, yes, O my dearest mother.
And with good cut and line."

"Spin, spin, O my darling daughter,
I'll buy you a man."
"Yes, yes, O my dearest mother.
Just as quick as you can.
Now I can be spinning,
No hurt to my finger,
Tra la, tra la,
There's never a pain!"

From "The World Sings." By permission of the publishers, The Year Book Press, Ltd., London, England.

THE SUN WORSHIPPERS

English version by
H.W. LOOMIS

United States - Zuni Indian

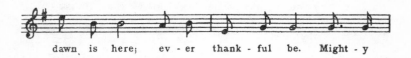

Rise,— a - rise,— a - rise!— (Rise, a - rise, a - rise!)

The dawn is here, day is call - ing thee. The

dawn is here; ev - er thank - ful be. Might - y

Day - god, he is watch - ing thee. Glo - rious

Life-god, he is guard-ing thee. _____

The above fine sample of a Zuni Indian melody is an excerpt from a song collected by Carlos Troyer which may be found in its entirety in the accredited source.
It should be sung with a very deliberate rhythm.

TEN THOUSAND MEN

WERE GOING ON MANOEUVRES

English version by
J. E. T.

German

1. Ten thou-sand men were go - ing on nan-oeuv - res,

Chorus

Ten thou-sand men were go - ing on man-oeuv - res, Di

zum ti di a, Di zum ti di a, were

go - ing on man-oeuv - res, Zum ti di a.

2. Marching to camp they met a working farmer.

3. This farmer had a fair and lovely daughter.

4. "Farmer, farmer, farmer, I would gladly court her."

5. "Soldier, soldier, soldier, how big is your fortune?"

6. "Farmer, farmer, farmer, two boots old and useless."

7. "Soldier, soldier, soldier, then you may not court her."

8. "Farmer, farmer, farmer, at home we have far fairer."

THERE'S NAE LUCK ABOUT THE HOUSE

Descant arranged by
GEOFFREY SHAW

1. And are ye sure the news is true? And are you sure he's
3. There are two hens up - on the bank Hae fed this month and

weel?   Is this a time to   talk o' wark? Ye
mair,   Mak' haste and thraw their   necks a - bout, That

jades, fling by your   wheel! Is   this a time to
Col - in weel may   fare; And spread the ta - ble

think o' wark, When Col - in's at the   door?   Gie
neat and clean, Gar   il - ka things look   braw;   For

Chorus

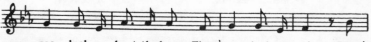

me my cloak, I'll to the quay, And see him come a-shore.⎫
wha can tell how Col - in fared, When he was far a - wa'. ⎬ For there's

nae luck a - bout the house, There's nae luck at a',   There's

lit-tle pleas-ure in the house, When our gude-man's a - wa'!

Descant
Ah ___ Ah ___

Melody
2. Rise up and mak' a clean fire-side, Put on the muc-kle pot; Gie
4. Come, gie me down my big-on-et, My bish-op-sat-in goon, And

Ah ___

lit-tle Kate her cot-ton gown, And Jock his Sun-day coat; And
rin and tell the Bail-lie's wife, That Col-in's come to toon; My

Ah ___

mak' their shoon as black as slaes, Their hose as white as snaw; It's
tur-key slip-pers maum gae on, My hose o' pearl blue, It's

Chorus
ff
For there's
ff

a' to please my ain gude-man, He likes to see them braw.
a' to please my ain gude-man, For he's both leal and true. } For there's

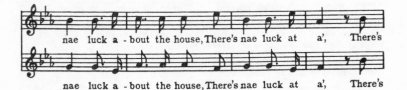

nae luck a-bout the house, There's nae luck at a', There's
nae luck a-bout the house, There's nae luck at a', There's

lit-tle pleas-ure in the house, When our gude-man's a wa'.

lit-tle pleas-ure in the house, When our gude-man's a - wa'.

Note that the descant it cleverly based upon another Scottish air, "The Blue Bells of Scotland."

By permission of the publishers, Novello and Company, Ltd., London, England. United States agent, The H. W. Gray Company, New York, N. Y.

THE OYSTER FISHERS' SONG

Scottish

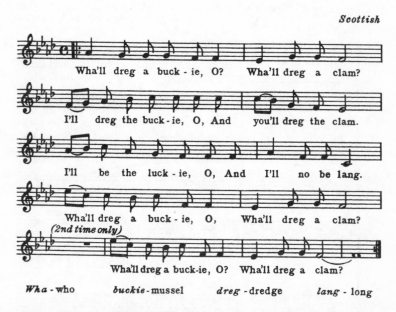

Wha'll dreg a buck-ie, O? Wha'll dreg a clam?

I'll dreg the buck-ie, O, And you'll dreg the clam.

I'll be the luck-ie, O, And I'll no be lang.

Wha'll dreg a buck-ie, O, Wha'll dreg a clam?

(2nd time only)

Wha'll dreg a buck-ie, O? Wha'll dreg a clam?

Wha - who   *buckie* - mussel   *dreg* - dredge   *lang* - long

This work-song is sung by the Scottish fisher-lassies who sing loudly about other kinds of shell-fish in order to deceive the oysters, their real prey.

Tune noted in 1903 by Mrs. Kennedy Fraser.
Words noted in 1933 by Miss. Isobel V. S. Dunlop.

Used by permission.

WILLIE, WILLIE WILL

Two part canon

English version by
J. E. T.   JOHANNES BRAHMS (1833 – 1897)

Wil-lie, Wil-lie, Will,   a   man   is   com - ing,

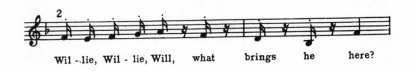

Wil - lie, Wil - lie, Will,   what   brings   he   here?

Wil - lie, Wil - lie, Will,   fine   sug - ar   wa - fers.

Wil - lie, Wil - lie, Will,   they're   for   a   child that's dear.

Willie, Willie, Will, say what else brings he?
Willie, Willie, Will, he hears a noise.
Willie, Willie, Will, a cane he carries,
Willie, Willie, Will, for naughty little boys.

Willie, Willie, Will, my child is good now,
Willie, Willie, Will, asleep he'll stay.
Willie, Willie, Will, my child is still now,
Willie, Willie, Will, just give that stick away!

Brahms founded this canon upon an old folksong and it should be sung "straight"
till it is very well-known. For effective performance it must be sung staccato.

WHIRLING MAIDEN

J.E.T.

Czech

Whirl-ing, turn-ing, whirl-ing, turn-ing, dance a-round me,

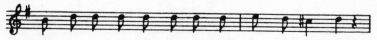

Whirl-ing, turn-ing, whirl-ing, turn-ing, dance a-round me;

Make a ring a-bout me, Do not go with-out me,

Then my dear-est, then my dear-est sweet-heart you'll be

If they find me, if they find me, they will catch me,
If they find me, if they find me, they will catch me;
Officers will take me,
In the barracks make me
Be a soldier, be a soldier, please pity me!

You my true one, you my dear, had pity on me,
You my true one, you my dear, had pity on me;
After me came riding,
Took me from my hiding
That in Brno, that in Brno safe we might be.

Brno - Brrrno   (Brno is the capital of Moravia.)

WHO COMES LAUGHING?

Three part round

This round can be used as a processional.

By permission, from Curwen Edition No. 6079, published by J. Curwen and Sons, Ltd., 24 Berners Street, London, W. 1. England.

WILL YE NO COME BACK AGAIN!

Scottish

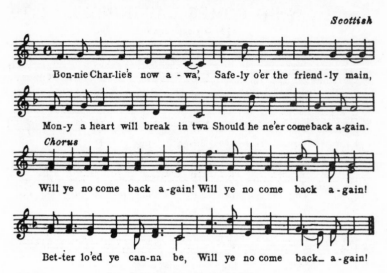

Bon-nie Char-lie's now a - wa', Safe-ly o'er the friend-ly main,

Mon-y a heart will break in twa Should he ne'er come back a-gain.

Chorus

Will ye no come back a-gain! Will ye no come back a-gain!

Bet-ter lo'ed ye can-na be, Will ye no come back a-gain!

> Sweet' the lav'rock's note and lang,
> Lilting wildly up the glen;
> But aye to me he sings ae sang, —
> "Will ye no come back again!"

Laverock - lark

This famous Cavalier song celebrated Prince Charlie's departure from Scotland. The second verse given here is often sung to speed the parting guest.

RALLY SONG
Four part rounnd

Balkan

Mil-ha bi - lou lou-bi shem-bel, mil-ha bi-lou lou-bi shem-bel,

mil-ha bi - lou lou-bi shem-bel, mil-ha bi - lou lou-bi shem-bel.

This stirring round is based upon a "getting together" song from the Balkan Peninsula. The leader first sings alone and continues to sing in a high register while the rest of the group, as they assemble, chant the lower notes. This gives an exciting effect. The round for our purpose is to be sung as written.

ZITHER AND I

English version by
J. E. T.

Italian

Tra la la la la, My zith-er I'm strum-ming,

Tra la la la la, The danc-ers are hum-ming,

Tra la la la la, Here's thanks for your wel-come,

Fine

Rov-ing gyp-sies are zith-er and I.

Tra la la la la, la la la la la la la,

rall   *D.C.*

Tra la la la la la la la la la la la.

NO HIDING PLACE

Mrs. Willa A. Townsend

Negro Spiritual

Lively

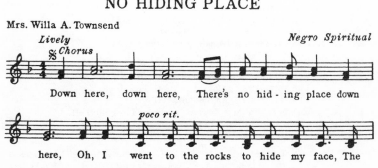

Down here, down here, There's no hid-ing place down

poco rit.

here, Oh, I went to the rocks to hide my face, The

NO HIDING PLACE (continued)

rocks cried out, "No hid-ing place", There's no hid-ing place down here. no hid-ing place down here.

1. Sin-ner man, you bet-ter re-pent. *(hm_____)* pent, *(hm_____)* O__ sin-ner man, you bet-ter re-pent, For God's going to call__ you__ to__ the__ judg-ment, There's no hid-ing place down here.

2. Sinner man, your heart's like steel, *(hm)*
Sinner man, your heart's like steel, *(hm)*
Sinner man, your heart's like steel,
But the fire in hell's going to make you feel,
There's no hiding place down here.

3. The sinner man gambled and fell, *(hm)*
The sinner man gambled and fell, *(hm)*
The sinner man gambled and fell,
He wanted to go to heaven, but he had to go to hell,
There's no hiding place down here.

From "Spirituals Triumphant", published by the Sunday School Publishing Board of the National Baptist Convention, A. M. Townsend, D. D., Secretary, Nashville, Tennessee.

COLIN

JOSEPH BOVET

Que vas-tu faire avec ce grain?
Que faire avec ce grain?
Avec ce grain je ferai du pain,
Ah, tu feras du pain?

Et ce bon pain qui le mangera?
Qui donc le mangera?
C'est moi quand la Bénichon viendra,
Ah, quel régal tu f'ras!

Bénichon – a Swiss feast-day for which a special sweet, white bread is made.

By special permission of Monsieur l'Abbé Bovet, Fribourg, Switzerland.

KOOKABURRA
Four part round

M. SINCLAIR   *Australian*

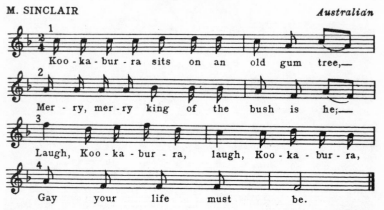

Koo-ka-bur-ra sits on an old gum tree,—

Mer-ry, mer-ry king of the bush is he;—

Laugh, Koo-ka-bur-ra, laugh, Koo-ka-bur-ra,

Gay your life must be.

The Kookaburra is a bird which has an eerie laugh; it is a great snake killer.
The gum tree is the eucalyptus.

Used by permission.

SWEET MUSIC ENCHANTING
from "The Magic Flute"

English version by
J. E. T.   MOZART (1756-1791)

Sweet mus-ic en-chant-ing falls soft on the

ear: La ra la, la, la, la, ra, la, la, la, la, ra, la! It

ban-ish-es trou-ble, our cares dis-ap-pear. La ra

la, la, la, la ra la ra, la, la ra la! It la!

This tune is played by Papageno, the birdcatcher, on his glockenspiel, a chime
of magic bells he uses in times of stress.

THE CHILDREN'S PRAYER

from "Hänsel and Gretel"

HUMPERDINCK (1854 - 1921)

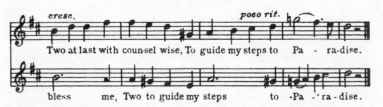

cresc. ... *poeo rit.*

Two at last with coun-sel wise, To guide my steps to Pa - ra-dise.

bless me, Two to guide my steps to ·Pa - ·ra-dise.

This is an example of a song from an opera largely based on folk material.

From "The World Sings." By permission of the publishers, The Year Book Press, Ltd., London, England.

SONG OF THE DELHI TONGAWALLAH
(Ponycart driver)

English version by
Miss GETSIE SAMUEL   *Hindustani*

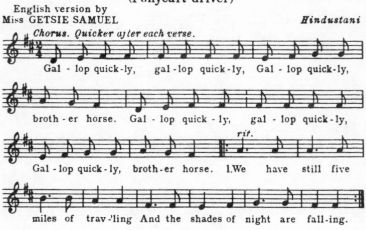

Chorus. Quicker after each verse.

Gal - lop quick-ly, gal - lop quick-ly, Gal - lop quick-ly,

broth - er horse. Gal - lop quick - ly, gal - lop quick - ly,

rit.

Gal - lop quick - ly, broth-er horse. 1.We have still five

miles of trav-'ling And the shades of night are fall-ing.

2.
    If cruel robbers do waylay us
    What to do then? What to do then?
    Gallop quickly etc.

3.
    Grain and grass be yours in plenty
    If we get home quickly, horse.
    Gallop quickly etc.

Indian children perform the above as an action song.
  During the *chorus* hold reins and seem to urge horse faster.
  During verse 1 show five fingers and describe an arc with right hand for second line.
  During verse 2 question neighbours anxiously.
  During verse 3 for "grain" cup hands, for "grass" pantomime "bundle," for "plenty" make sign for "big."
  During last chorus rise from seats and "drive" furiously.

F. S. PIERPOINT   J. S. BACH (1685 - 1750)

For the beau ty of the— earth, _____ For the beau-ty of— the skies, For the love which from our birth o ver and a-round us lies, Lord, our God, to Thee we raise _____

This our sac - ri - fice of praise.

For the beauty of each hour
Of the day and of the night,
Hill and vale, tree and flow'r,
Sun and moon and stars of light.

For the joy of ear and eye,
For the heart and mind's delight,
For the mystic harmony
Linking sense to sound and sight.

For the joy of human love,
Brother, sister, parent, child,
Friends on earth and friends above,
For all gentle thoughts and mild.

For each perfect gift of Thine
To our race so freely given,
Graces human and divine,
Flow'rs of earth and buds of heaven.

From "**24 Bach Chorales**" published by Paterson's Publications, Ltd., London, England. By permission.

RIDDLE SONG

United States - Kentucky

Not too quickly

I gave my love a cher - ry that has no stone, I gave my love a chick - en that has no bone, I gave my love a ring— that has no end, I gave my love a ba - by that's no cry - en.

How can there be a cherry that has no stone?
How can there be a chicken that has no bone?
How can there be a ring that has no end?
How can there be a baby with no cry 'en?

A cherry when it's blooming, it has no stone,
A chicken when it's pipping, it has no bone,
A ring when it's rolling, it has no end,
A baby when it's sleeping, there s no cry 'en.

pipping - hatching

BRIGHTLY, BRIGHTLY GLEAM THE SPARKLING RILLS
from "The Seasons"

JOSEPH HAYDN (1732 – 1809)

Allegretto

Bright - ly, bright - ly, gleam the spark - ling rills, Sum - mer, sum - mer, sleeps on ver - dant hills.

Semi Chorus

A - mid the shades we ram - bling stray, Where cool - ing foun - tains spor - tive___ play.

Chorus

Peal - ing, peal - ing, come the laugh and

BRIGHTLY, BRIGHTLY GLEAM THE SPARKLING RILLS (continued)

shout; While gai - ly we sing till the

old for - ests ring, While gai - ly we sing till the

old for - ests ring With the joy of our mer - ry

rout, With the joy of our mer - ry rout.

Odors, odors, load the summer air,
Music, music, sweetly echoes there,
And brightest maids with softest glance
Then join the song and lead the dance.

Faintly, faintly sounds the distant fall,
Lightly, lightly, distant echoes call,
And in their voice we seem to hear
The tones of friends both gay and dear.

From the Franklin Square Song Collection, Number 2, by permission of the publishers, Harper and Brothers, New York, N.Y.

FINLANDIA

(from the Tone Poem)

English text by
FRANCES B. GAINES

JEAN SIBELIUS

O! land of ours, to thee we raise our prais-es,—— O! Na-tive land where lakes re-flect the sky.—— In for-est groves the pine and larch are grow-ing—— A-bove thy plains the moun-tains stand high.—— O! land of ours, with beau-ty God has blessed thee.— We shall keep strong; our faith shall not die.

From out thy soil a glorious race has risen;
For freedom's cause thy sons have fought and won:
And may we hold this past of ours for ever
Within our hearts as bright as the sun;
Thee may we serve as thy true sons forever.
Keep faith in God, whose will shall be done.

Words from "Keep on Singing." Published by the Paull-Pioneer Music Corporation, New York. By permission.

EASTER ALLELUYA

Arranged by IVOR ATKINS

In moderate time; dignified

Al - le - lu - ya, al - le - lu - ya!

Org.

O___ praise Him, O___ praise Him,___ Al - le -

Unison

lu - ya, al - le - lu - ya, al - le - lu - - ya!

All creatures of our God and King,
Lift up your voice and with us sing
   Alleluya, alleluya!
Thou burning sun with golden beam,
Thou silver moon with softer gleam:

     O praise Him, O praise Him,
     Alleluya, alleluya, alleluya!

Thou rushing wind that art so strong,
Ye clouds that sail in heav'n along,
   O praise Him, alleluya!
Thou rising morn, in praise rejoice.
Ye lights of evening, find a voice:

Thou flowing water, pure and clear,
Make music for thy Lord to hear,
   Alleluya, alleluya!
Thou fire so masterful and bright,
That givest man both warmth and light:

Dear mother earth, who day by day
Unfoldest blessings on our way,
   O praise Him, alleluya!
The flowers and fruits that in thee grow,
Let them His glory also show:

And all ye men of tender heart,
Forgiving others, take your part,
   O sing ye, alleluya!
Ye who long pain and sorrow bear,
Praise God and on Him cast your care:

          W. H. DRAPER 1855–1933
          based on ST. FRANCIS 1182–1226

THE HEAVENS RESOUND

ANDREAS HOFER   Arr. from BEETHOVEN (1770–1827)

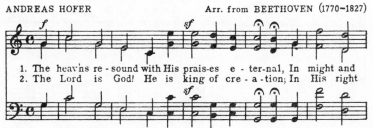

1. The heav'ns re-sound with His prais-es e-ter-nal, In might and
2. The Lord is God! He is king of cre-a-tion; In His right

glo-ry they com - bine To tell His name thro' earth and the
hand He holds them all, His chil-dren, we, in love and de-

o - ceans That man may hear the word di - vine. He holds the
vo - tion, Be - fore His might and pow - er fall. O Fa - ther,

suns in the blue vault-ed heav-ens, He plants his foot up-on the
hear! we,Thy sons,bring our blessings, Our pray'r-ful thanks to Thee we

world; The myr - iad stars bow in will - ing sub-jec-tion; The
raise; The heav'ns re - sound; break; O earth, in-to glo - ry, To

u - ni-verse His hand un-furl'd. The u - ni-verse His hand un-furl'd.
serve! a - dore! and sing His praise! To serve! a - dore! and sing His praise!

* The accompaniment here has 1, 4 and 3 beats interlude, omitted here for lack of space.

From "Twice 55 plus Community Songs." C. C. Birchard and Company, owners of the copyright. By permission.

ROSE, ROSE

Four part round

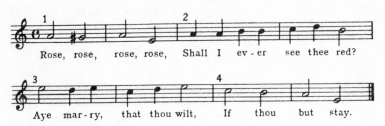

Rose, rose, rose, rose, Shall I ev-er see thee red?

Aye mar-ry, that thou wilt, If thou but stay.

NOW IS THE MONTH OF MAYING

THOMAS MORLEY, (1557-1603)

1. Now is the month of May - ing, When
2. The Spring, clad all in glad - ness, Doth

mer - ry lads are play - ing,{ Fa la la la la la
laugh at Win-ter's sad - ness,}

la la la, fa la la la la la la.

Each with his bon - ny lass, A
And to the bag - pipes' sound The

danc - ing on the grass. } Fa la la la la,
nymphs tread out the ground. }

Dal ℅

fa la la la la la la la la la la la.

HARK! HARK! THE LARK

SHAKESPEARE

FRANZ SCHUBERT (1797 - 1828)

Hark! hark! the lark at heav'n's gate sings, And Phoe-bus 'gins - a - rise His steeds to wa - ter at those springs On chal - ic'd flow'rs that lies on chal-ic'd flow'rs that lies; And wink - ing Ma - ry - buds be - gin To ope their gold - en eyes; With ev - 'ry - thing that pret - ty bin, My la - dy sweet, a - rise, With ev - 'ry-thing that pret-ty bin, My la - dy sweet, a - rise, a - rise, a - rise, my la - dy sweet, a - rise, a - rise, a - rise, my la - dy sweet, a - rise!

Marybuds - marigolds

This song occurs in "Cymbeline." It is sung by musicians outside Imogen's apartment at the behest of Cloten who wishes thus to woo her.

ONCE TO EVERY MAN AND NATION

Welsh tune Ton-y-Botel

JAMES RUSSELL LOWELL

T. J. WILLIAMS

Once to ev-'ry man and na-tion Comes the mo-ment
In the strife of truth with falsehood For the good or

to de-cide Some great cause, God's new Mes-si-ah,
e-vil side;

Of-fer-ing each the bloom or blight, And the choice goes

by for-ev-er 'Twixt that dark-ness and that light.

Then to side with truth is noble,	Though the cause of evil prosper,
When we share her wretched crust,	Yet 'tis truth alone is strong;
Ere her cause bring fame and profit,	Though her portion be the scaffold,
And 'tis prosperous to be just;	And upon the throne be wrong—
Then it is the brave man chooses,	Yet that scaffold sways the future,
While the coward stands aside,	And behind the dim unknown,
And the multitude make virtue	Standeth God within the shadow,
Of the faith they had denied.	Keeping watch above his own.

From "The Present Crisis" written by Lowell in 1844 as a protest against war with Mexico.

Music arrangement by permission of W. Gwenlyn Evans and Son, Caernavon, Wales.

O COME, ALL YE FAITHFUL

ARRANGED WITH DESCANT

"ADESTE FIDELES" *Anon. 18th Century*

1. O come, all ye faith-ful, Joy-ful and tri-umph-ant; O
2. *f* God of God, Light of light,
4. *f* Yea, Lord, we greet Thee, Born this hap-py morn-ing;

come ye, O come ye to Beth - le - hem;
p Lo!— He ab - hors not the Vir - gin's womb;
Je - su, to Thee be glo - ry given;

Come and be - hold Him Born, the King of An-gels;
f Ve - ry God, Be - got - ten, not cre - a - ted;
Word of the Fa - ther, Now in flesh ap - pear-ing;

come, let us a - dore Him, O come, let us a - dore Him, O

O COME, ALL YE FAITHFUL (continued)

come, let us a - dore Him, — Christ — the Lord.

Descant

3. Sing, choirs of an - gels, Sing with ex - ul - ta - tion,

Melody

3. Sing, choirs of an - gels, Sing with ex - ul - ta - tion,

Sing, all ye cit - i - zens of heaven a - bove, Glo - ry to

Sing, all ye cit - i - zens of heaven a - bove

O COME, ALL YE FAITHFUL (continued)

God, _____ glo-ry to God In_ the high-est!

Glo-ry to God _____ In the_ high-est! O

O come, let us a-dore Him, O

come, let us a-dore Him, O come, let us a-dore Him, O

come, _____ let us a-dore Him, Christ the Lord.

come, let us a-dore Him,_ Christ the Lord.

DECK THE HALL

Old Welsh Carol

Joyfully; with spirit

Deck the hall with boughs of hol - ly,

Fa la la la la la la la la. 'Tis the sea - son

to be jol - ly, Fa la la la la la

la la la. Don we now our gay ap-par - el,

Fa la la la la la la la la, Troll the an - cient

Christ - mas car - ol, Fa la la la la la la la la.

See the blazing yule before us,
Strike the harp and join the chorus,
Follow me in merry measure,
While I tell of Christmas treasure.

Fast away the old year passes,
Hail the new! ye lads and lasses;
Sing we joyous all together,
Heedless of the wind and weather.

I SAW THREE SHIPS

Descant Arranged by
H. A. CHAMBERS

*2. And what was in those ships all three,
On Christmas day, on Christmas day?
And what was in those ships all three,
On Christmas day in the morning?

3. The Virgin Mary and Christ were there,
On Christmas day, on Christmas day;
The Virgin Mary and Christ were there,
On Christmas day in the morning.

*4. Pray, whither sailed those ships all three,
On Christmas day, on Christmas day?
Pray, whither sailed those ships all three,
On Christmas day in the morning?

5. O they sailed into Bethlehem,
On Christmas day, on Christmas day;
O they sailed into Bethlehem,
On Christmas day in the morning.

6. And all the bells on earth shall ring,
On Christmas day, on Christmas day;
And all the bells on earth shall ring,
On Christmas day in the morning.

* It is suggested that these verses be sung as a solo or by a few voices.

Descant

7. And all the An-gels in Heaven shall sing, On

Melody

7. And all the An-gels in Heaven shall sing, On

Christ-mas day, on Christ-mas day; And all the An-gels in

Christ-mas day, on Christ-mas day; And all the An-gels in

Heaven shall sing, On Christ-mas day in the morn-ing.

Heaven shall sing, On Christ-mas day in the morn-ing.

9. Then let us all re - joice a - main, On Christ-mas day, on Christ-mas day; Then let us all re-joice a - main, On Christ-mas day in the morn - ing.

9. Then let us all re - joice a - main, On Christ-mas day, On Christ-mas day; Then let us all re-joice a - main, On Christ-mas day in the morn - ing.

ff marcato

rall. molto

By permission of the publishers, Novello and Company, Ltd., London, England.
United States agent, The H. W. Gray Company, New York, N. Y.

WHERE HAVE YOU BEEN WALKING, SHEPHERDESS?

English version by
   J. E. T.

French-Canadian

Where have you been walk-ing shep-herd - ess?

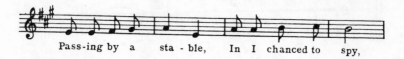

Pass-ing by a sta - ble, In I chanced to spy,

Saw a scene of won - der, There be-fore my eye.

Tell us what you saw there, shepherdess
Snugly in the manger,
   Deep within the straw
Wrapped with hands so tender,
   I a Baby saw.

Was there nothing further, shepherdess?
Holy Mother Mary
   Gave the Infant food;
By them Holy Joseph
   Cold and shiv'ring stood.

Was there nothing further, shepherdess?
Just beside the manger,
   Two beasts kind and mild,
Ox and ass together
   Breathed and warmed the Child.

Was there nothing further, shepherdess?
Yes, I saw three angels
   Come down from the sky.
Singing loud the praises
   Of the Lord most High.

VESPER HYMN

THOMAS MOORE *Russian*

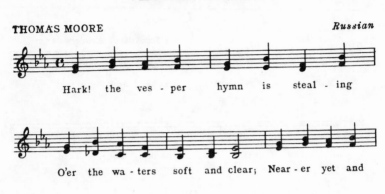

Hark! the ves - per hymn is steal - ing

O'er the wa - ters soft and clear; Near - er yet and

near - er peal - ing, Soft it breaks up - on the ear.

Chorus

Ju - bi - la - te, Ju - bi - la - te,

Ju - bi - la - te, A - men.

Now like moonlight waves retreating,
To the shore it dies along;
Now like angry surges meeting,
Breaks the mingled tide of song.

Once again sweet voices ringing,
Louder still the music swells;
While on summer breezes winging,
Comes the chime of vesper bells.

SIX GRACES

I

Second voice enters here

Morn - ing, ev' - ning, noon and night, For

all Thy gifts we thank Thee, Lord.

II

Hark to the chimes,

Come bow your head, We thank Thee,

Lord, For this good bread.

III

Morn - ing
Noon - time } is here, the board is spread,
Eve - ning

Thanks be to God, Who gives us bread.

IV

Two part grace

1st Voice

For this our dai - ly food, For

2nd Voice

For

health and hap - pi - ness, Give us a thank - ful

this our dai - ly food, For health and hap - pi -

heart, A thank - ful heart, dear Lord, dear Lord.

ness, Give us a thank - ful heart dear Lord.

V

THE WAYFARER'S GRACE

M. ELIZABETH WORSFOLD   G. C. E. RYLEY

For all the glo - ry of the Way,

For Thy pro - tec - tion night and day,

For roof - tree, fire, —— and bed, and board,

For friends, and home, —— we thank Thee, Lord.

By permission of Miss Worsfold and Canon Ryley

Copyright 1938 by The Kent Girl Guides Association; from the Kent County Hymn Book and the Kent County Song Book.

VI

MARIE GAUDETTE

God has cre - a - ted a new day,

Sil - ver and green and gold;

Live that the sun - set may find us

Wor - thy His gift to hold.

NOTES FOR SONG LEADERS

NOTES FOR SONG LEADERS

HAVE been prepared to help recreational song leaders who have had little or no musical training. The practical suggestions herein contained are the result of many years' experience and observation in the field of social music.

SELECTION OF MATERIAL

THERE is no dearth of material for amateur voices of all ages; the task of the leader is to select from the wealth of good, bad, and indifferent material songs that have artistic value, are attractive, and lie within the vocal range and ability of the group. With a new group it is well to start with songs that are quickly learned; for instance, those that have short verses and a long chorus, or those that build up interest by addition or repetition. Once confidence is gained through songs of this simpler kind, music of a more ambitious nature may be attempted. There are three main types of song suitable for recreational purposes:

1. *Folk Songs* are of unknown origin, orally transmitted by generations of singers; they are a priceless heritage. Their stability is due to the frequent beauty of their melodies and the sincerity of their thought. Folk songs are fundamentally human and wholesome; by singing those of our own country we carry on a proud tradition; by learning those of other lands we widen our world knowledge, for song is a universal language. Under the heading of folk songs we may group traditional ballads and carols, lullabies, shanties, spirituals, work songs, singing games, street cries, and other types—enough to last many a lifetime.

2. *Rounds and Canons* are popular with young and old; they afford a painless even joyful introduction to part singing; they are a team game and a good discipline for "wobblers." In the case of long or difficult rounds it is sometimes better to teach them first as straight songs and then in two parts only, before proceeding to the maximum number of parts. (This is always possible; the second voice comes in at the same point, whether the round is sung in two parts or twenty.) A variety in round singing may be achieved by ending all parts together instead of having them trail off one after the other. The singers are kept on their toes if they have to look out for a sudden "hold" signal, which gives a satisfying chord conclusion. The amateur leader will have no difficulty in deciding where a stop is possible if he or she listens to one particular group and gives the signal when that group has reached the exact end of the round.

3. *Art Songs*. Art songs may be chosen from compositions of the masters and are often well within the reach of amateur groups; singing well this type of song leads to a greater understanding of music in a wider field. For example, Beethoven's "Ode to Joy," and "The Children's Prayer" from *Hänsel and Gretel*, give respectively an introduction to symphonic and operatic music; from such simple beginnings a real appreciation of high-grade music may be stimulated. Children can not be expected to have taste for what they never experience and

the same holds true for adults whose musical education has been meager. There is no need for the amateur to be frightened by the name of a great composer attached to a song; often the greatest people are the simplest.

BUILDING GOOD TRADITIONS

PATIENCE, skill, and tact are required to break down poor singing traditions. It is difficult to wean children, and adults too, from poor songs to which they have become passionately attached. Example is better than precept; if one can substitute a good song for a poor one—a song that will supply the same need or fit in with the same mood—the good song, given an equal chance, will probably win the day. The insidious part of cheap music is its "catchiness," but plenty of wholesome folk tunes are also catchy without seeming in the least highbrow. Sentimentality is another aspect to avoid in singing. Art is never mawkish. If the song itself is really fine, good-natured bantering and a shortly worded constructive criticism will usually put the singing right; if the song is poor suggest one that expresses true sentiment as opposed to sentimentality, one that has enduring strength and invokes strength as opposed to false emotionalism. No one appreciates what is half known or understood; a miraculous change of taste can not be expected but perseverance on the part of the leader and faith in the material will be ultimately rewarded. What is artistically valuable must in the end prevail against the shoddy and the superficial.

PLANNING A SONG PROGRAM

A BALANCED program may contain: (a) A few well known songs. (b) New material easily learned such as simple rounds or songs having "catchy" tunes and strong rhythm. (c) Songs presenting a challenge. (d) A closing group of especially fine songs, probably of the quieter type. The first two classes warm up the more apathetic singers and at the same time enable the lively ones to "let off steam." At the height of the program, with everybody tuned up, real work may be done on the more difficult material. The concluding songs give a sense of relaxation and are a satisfying culmination to the group experience. Not all the verses of every song need be sung unless the continuity of a story is thereby marred; the extra time available may be used to gain at least passing acquaintance with still more material. The wise leader ends the program while enthusiasm is still high; songs of varying type, nationality, mood, and tempo have been offered; the group has been kept absolutely on the alert by the alertness of the leader; a fine program has not been allowed to peter out through overdoing.

PRESENTING A SONG TO THE GROUP

A GOOD SONG is made doubly interesting to singers if it is well presented. What is its background? Does it tell a story, suggest action, invite one to dance, or merely reflect a mood? Can it be dramatized or will it be good for shadowgraph presentation? A song may strike people in different ways; a study of its implications and of its highlights may open a dozen vistas of thought and cause one to see endless possibilities as to its use in a program.

Analysis. The form of a new song is grasped more quickly if the leader gives a very brief analysis of the tune, or a few pointers such as where repetitions occur, where a new phrase begins in relation to the preceding phrase, or where a change of key occurs. If these hints, however, have to develop into lengthy explanations they may as well be omitted for they may only confuse an amateur group.

Rendition. Accuracy, clear enunciation, good rhythm, variety of expression and tempo, and last but not least, fine tone quality are the goals of chorus work. No one voice should predominate (least of all the leader's), but all be blended to produce a high standard of communal achievement giving satisfaction to all concerned. A good attack is important: the leader announces clearly the title of the song, gives the first note, and then with everyone's mind on the alert the group is ready for a clean start. The release should be equally neat.

Common faults in general group singing are dragging, poor articulation, shouting, and scooping from one note to another. Even a slow song can give a feeling of movement and should express vitality as opposed to deadness. A mumbling enunciation is eliminated if (a) care is taken to ensure that the singers are word perfect and not relying upon their neighbors; (b) the singers are encouraged to use their mouths and facial muscles more than they do in ordinary speech. It is a good plan occasionally to ask a friendly visitor to stand at the back of the room to see if every word of an unfamiliar song is understandable, even if the singing is very soft.

Pitch is important for tone quality; if a song is pitched too low for children it coarsens their voices and as a constant practice does irreparable harm; moreover, the song takes on an unpleasant growling effect. If the pitch is given a little higher than is comfortable for the adult leader, the younger singers will probably be in their correct vocal range, and the songs all the easier to keep controlled in volume and clear in tone. Modulation from soft to loud and loud to soft is fun to do and is at the same time a training in flexibility; nothing is more deadening than a dreary monotony of tone. All songs have downward and upward curves, none are meant to be interpreted as a straight line. A leader who indicates the highlights of a song and encourages an interest in the finer points of shading will soon have a group really appreciative of artistic values.

A quick response to rhythm may be obtained by having the singers walk out the beat of a song, sway in their seats, or clap. If it is a work song, going through the motions of heaving, hauling, hammering, or paddling will give an effect of realism, intensify the feeling for accent, and get the tune going in its proper swing.

Part Singing may be sometimes obtained quite satisfactorily by spontaneous harmonizing in such songs as Negro spirituals and others that lend themselves easily to this treatment, either by actual note reading or, where no music is available, by taking time to teach parts by rote. Quite often an alto or tenor part has a definite melody that may be learned in a very few minutes. The same is true of many descants. "Descanting," or singing apart, is an ancient harmonic device in which a contrasting melody is carried above the treble part of a song by a few clear, high voices (not more than a third of the total number of singers, otherwise the main tune is lost), and this offers an especially welcome diversion in the case of long hymns or very well known folk songs. Descant singing should be reserved for one or two verses only of a song, otherwise the "surprise" effect is lost; it should leave both audience and singers wanting more. With amateurs and children it is an effective beginning in "singing apart" for the higher voices, as generally the lower voices have all the fun of harmonizing.

Singing Unaccompanied and by Rote. The purest form of choral singing is *a cappella,* or without accompaniment. Folk songs from earliest times were sung unaccompanied; sailors, Negroes, and other people working in the open have a fine sense of pitch because they do not rely upon instrumental support. The piano has no place at the campfire; as the singers gain confidence their unaccompanied group singing will, in a short time, become amazingly true and improved in quality. For variety, campfire music may sometimes be accompanied by such unsophisticated instruments as shepherds' pipes, banjos, accordions, or guitars, but these additions are merely a pleasurable diversion and should not be a prop for vocal weaknesses.

Singing by rote is ideal for informal occasions. If singers have to keep peering into books there is less joyousness in their singing; also their attention can not be entirely concentrated on the leader. Learning by heart with facility is merely a matter of practice; the leader first sings a new song so that the group knows what the song is about and how it sounds; the first verse is then taught phrase by phrase (if the words alone are taught first, they become divorced from their natural association with the tune). Once a verse is learned the rest is easy.

Listening. Too little opportunity has been paid to "listening" in recreational singing although it does provide a real opportunity to stimulate a critical faculty. In these days of having music literally poured over us from the ether and elsewhere we should help our singers know what to listen for and how to develop a sensitivity of hearing. Have the group occasionally criticize itself when a song is ended; or during the performance of a number, let one or two members listen to the song from a distance. They can say what sounds pleasing or otherwise; children like to do this kind of critical listening and often show surprising discrimination. Careful listening not only improves the ear but helps us avoid future pitfalls in our own musical activities; at the same time we can really appreciate the fine vocal achievements in others when we know from our own small experiences what effort is entailed to produce splendid singing.

BEATING TIME

THE FIRST beats in any time are the strong ones (i.e., the first notes after the bar lines) and this is indicated by bringing the hand straight down with a decisive gesture.

Two-beat time may be indicated down, up, thus—and this may also apply to 6/8 time, when it is a quick march tempo and therefore easily felt in two's.

Three-beat time is a triangular beat, down, out, up, thus—

Four-beat or common time is down, left, right, up, thus—

Slow six-eight time (rather unusual) is down, short left, short left; right, short right, up, thus—

These are not arbitrary rules, however; the main thing is to make the pulse of a song felt.

The right hand keeps the rhythm going; the left indicates expression, entrance of parts and so on. Volume may also be directed by the large or small beating of the right hand. Songs with strong rhythm require incisive beats, those with a flowing melody more rounded and smoother movements. Conducting should be very definite with the hands well under control. Drooping, flabby gestures will get a similar response in the singing. On the other hand small campfire or other intimate groups should not need very obvious conducting; once the songs are known the rhythm may even be indicated by a slight swaying of the body; facial expression, too, helps a great deal. A real feeling for rhythm and an intelligent interpretation of a song should come from within, rather than without;

happy indeed is the leader whose singers give spontaneous expression to individual and group sensitivity.

CORRELATING MUSIC WITH OTHER PROGRAM ACTIVITIES

THE ARTS should not be pigeon-holed; whenever it is possible in a natural and unforced way music should be correlated with other group activities. Folk songs and ballads are often capable of dramatization by human characters or of shadow-graph presentation. Often a song leader's ingenuity and imagination are called upon to supply incidental songs in keeping with the action, place, mood, and period of a play even though the original play does not call for music.

By making shepherd's pipes or other primitive instruments a link is forged between music and handicraft; by decorating them design may be practiced. If we dance to these instruments we have another happy combination of the arts. In the making of shadowgraphs we have still another obvious correlation of music, handicraft, and dramatics. There are hundreds of songs suitable for nature programs and lovely voyageur songs aid the rhythm and spirit of canoeing trips. Outdoor songs with strong rhythm lighten the hiker's journeyings and there are songs of the open range for those who ride. Camp songs composed as such by amateurs are generally quite limited in spirit, imagination, and skill but there is the whole world of real music upon which to draw, expressing the entire range of life's experience at its best. There is hardly an outdoor activity that can not be readily expressed in song; it is always possible to find music to fit the mood even if the song does not describe literally the activity itself.

THE LEADER'S REPERTORY

IT IS an important part of the song leader's task to keep a varied repertory and to be able to supply the right song for a given need, or at least to know where such a song is likely to be found. A leader whose collection is not constantly being increased is likely to become stale and limited; it is important to be ever on the alert to enrich one's own knowledge and indirectly that of the singers. The study of standard collections in libraries, discriminate listening to concert and radio performances, even pricking up one's ears to snatches of song heard in out-of-the-way places may provide the basis of an ever-enlarging musical knowledge and the acquisition of untold treasure.

Occasionally a good song does not make a quick appeal; thumbing through an accredited source book sometimes yields immediate disappointment. In this case single out one or two possible numbers and give them a chance to grow on you; sing them once or twice a day, then if they are first-rate they will gradually endear themselves to you just as a shy or diffident person sometimes improves upon acquaintance. A passing knowledge or of a deep liking for a song, however, is not sufficient for teaching it. One must be absolutely note and word perfect and have an intelligent understanding of its possibilities and difficulties. Only after a song has been mastered from every angle is the leader ready to present it to others; good leadership is sure leadership. Collecting songs is not enough; one must be able to pass them on with sureness and conviction.

RESPECT AND OBSERVANCE OF COPYRIGHTS

PERSONS of undoubted integrity have sometimes infringed copyright laws through sheer ignorance. The average person is generally vague about the subject and it is essential for song leaders to have a clear idea of the use and abuse of printed music matter. It is only fair to give due recognition to collectors, composers, arrangers, translators, and publishers for music which they make available to us. The law specifies that copyrighted material may not be copied by hand, mimeo-graphed, or reprinted without the publisher's permission and when a permission is granted it applies to that specific occasion only. Radio restrictions have been increasingly severe with regard to the use of copyright material, which makes it even more important for persons responsible for programs to ascertain the source of each song used. Besides protecting the composer or collector this restriction has another value since it discourages leaders from using dubious songs for which the sources can not be traced. An authentic song can generally be accredited to some standard collection. By being meticulous in recognizing sources a song leader is not only spared trouble but may be both an ethical and educational example to the group.

SUMMARY

SOCIAL singing is a release from mental and emotional tension; it makes one outgoing instead of self-centered. Its main object, enjoyment, should be made as rich and persistent as possible. However informal or spontaneous, good group singing has a certain cultural value whereas "noise-making" is an utterly profit-less pastime. The leader thus has a double responsibility—to ensure that the singers have a good time as well as an experience of enduring satisfaction. Members of a group are flattered if the leader expects the best from them and will respond to constructive criticism when carried away by an infectious enthusiasm that makes them really interested in their own progress.

To summarize a few pointers for song leaders:

1. Establish a congenial atmosphere and avoid mannerisms.

2. Be enthusiastic and forget self. The leader's undivided attention must be focused on every aspect of the song of the moment and the group's reaction to it.

3. Check up on mistakes as you go along. It is easier to make a correction early in the proceedings than it is later on.

4. Adopt a positive attitude and be encouraging but never praise a poor job.

5. Be good humored; discipline your group by cajolery into a high standard of performance, or at least into a will for a high standard.

6. Be patient under trying circumstances.

7. Avoid rigidity of program. Be prepared to change plans.

8. Do not be overly ambitious but keep your objective just a little ahead of the group, so that there is always something to strive for.

9. Show a respect for your art by refusing to identify yourself with what is musically in poor taste.

10. In general, aim at singing with spirit that does not deteriorate into raucousness, and with expression that does not degenerate into ultra-soulfulness.

Reprinted by permission of Girl Scouts, New York, N. Y.